basic
electronics

by VAN VALKENBURGH,
NOOGER & NEVILLE, INC.

VOL. 3

JOHN F. RIDER PUBLISHER, INC., NEW YORK
a division of HAYDEN PUBLISHING COMPANY, INC.

PREFACE

The texts of the entire Basic Electricity and Basic Electronics courses, as currently taught at Navy specialty schools, have now been released by the Navy for civilian use. This educational program has been an unqualified success. Since April, 1953, when it was first installed, over 25,000 Navy trainees have benefited by this instruction and the results have been outstanding.

The unique simplification of an ordinarily complex subject, the exceptional clarity of illustrations and text, and the plan of presenting one basic concept at a time, without involving complicated mathematics, all combine in making this course a better and quicker way to teach and learn basic electricity and electronics.

In releasing this material to the general public, the Navy hopes to provide the means for creating a nation-wide pool of pre-trained technicians, upon whom the Armed Forces could call in time of national emergency, without the need for precious weeks and months of schooling.

Perhaps of greater importance is the Navy's hope that through the release of this course, a direct contribution will be made toward increasing the technical knowledge of men and women throughout the country, as a step in making and keeping America strong.

Van Valkenburgh, Nooger and Neville, Inc.

New York, N. Y.
February, 1955

TABLE OF CONTENTS

VOL. 3 — BASIC ELECTRONICS

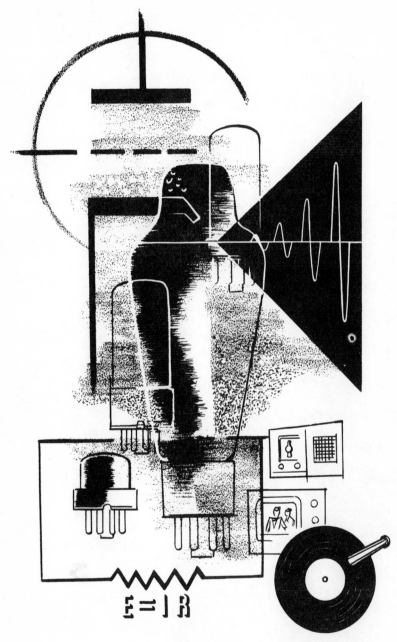

$E = IR$

Video Amplifiers

Introduction to Video Amplifiers

Video amplifiers are very similar to the RC-coupled audio amplifiers you have already seen. One very important difference between them is this— video amplifiers are designed to amplify odd-looking wave forms which an ordinary audio amplifier would distort. Some of the wave forms that video amplifiers are required to handle are called "pulses" or "square waves".

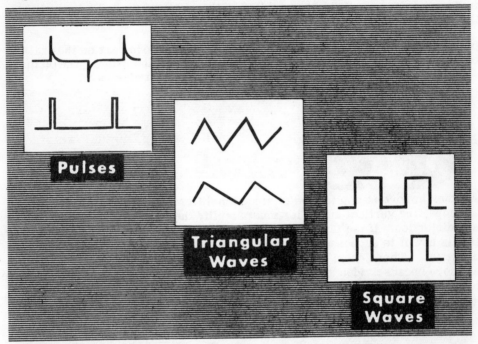

A French mathematician, Fourier, showed that such wave forms can be considered to be the sum of many sine waves of different frequencies. Some of the sine waves that the mathematicians say can be found in a square wave are ten times higher in frequency than the square wave itself. Therefore, the amplifier that is needed to amplify the square wave without distortion must have a frequency range covering the frequency of the square wave (fundamental) and the frequencies (harmonics) of all the other sine waves which make up the square wave.

However, all this about harmonic frequencies does not mean that you will need an advanced course in mathematics in order to understand video amplifiers. The mathematician can go right on defining a video amplifier as a wide-band amplifier capable of amplifying sine wave signals in the frequency range of from 30 cycles all the way up to several million cycles (megacycles) per second. You can look at it in a much simpler, and just as accurate, way. A video amplifier must be able to amplify signals such as square waves without adding distortion. Simple? If you put a square wave into a video amplifier you should get a square wave output. If not, something is wrong with the amplifier.

You will find video amplifiers used wherever square waves or pulses are to be amplified without distortion.

Introduction to Video Amplifiers (continued)

To many of you, the word "video" is synonymous with television and it should, therefore, come as no surprise to you to learn that video amplifiers are used in television receivers. The picture is sent out by the station as a series of electrical pulses which represent dark and light portions of the picture. These pulses are received in the home by the TV antenna, amplified by the video amplifier and applied to the picture tube so as to duplicate the picture sent out by the station.

In television, the characteristics of the picture depend in part on the quality of the video amplifier. If the amplifier distorted the pulses, the picture would lack the sharpness and the detail it would otherwise have.

Another important application of video amplifiers is in the oscilloscope. In a 'scope, the vertical amplifier must amplify the input signal without adding any distortion. If the input signal is a distorted sine wave or a square wave, that is how it is supposed to appear on the 'scope screen if the 'scope is to do its job. Therefore a video amplifier is used as the vertical amplifier in a 'scope because video amplifiers are capable of amplifying almost any wave form without distortion.

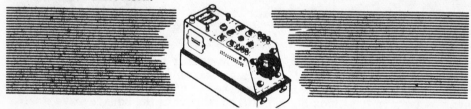

One of the very important applications of video amplifiers is in radar equipment. Every radar, whether it is used for search or for fire control, contains a video amplifier. Radar echoes are sharp pulses and the amplifier must preserve the shape of these echoes so that the radar operator can obtain accurate information about the target that is sending back the echo.

Only video amplifiers can be used where pulses or square waves are to be amplified without distortion. No other amplifier comes close to meeting the requirements for the video amplifiers in oscilloscopes, television, sonar, radar, teletype, loran and photo facsimile equipment.

Distortion of Square Waves

One reason that a square wave would be distorted in an audio amplifier is the amplifier's poor low frequency response. This shows up in the output as an unfaithful reproduction of the flat portion of the square wave.

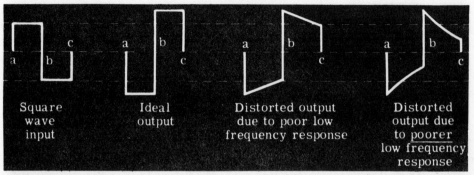

Square wave input

Ideal output

Distorted output due to poor low frequency response

Distorted output due to poorer low frequency response

This is what happens in the amplifier. During the flat portion of the square wave between time (a) and time (b) the grid voltage, the plate current and the plate voltage remain constant. At time (b), the grid voltage drops suddenly to a new value and the plate voltage rises just as suddenly to its new value.

When this happens, current will flow through R-2 in the direction shown, causing the output voltage to appear across this resistor. The amount of current that flows in R-2 depends, of course, on the value of the plate voltage, on the voltage across the coupling condenser and on the value of R-2. This current will be small if R-2 is large but, however small the current is, it will still charge up C-1 and thereby change the voltage across the condenser. As the voltage across C-1 increases, the current through R-2 decreases, resulting in the distorted output shown above.

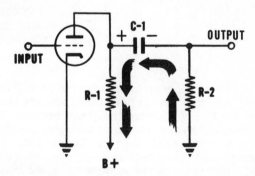

If C-1 has a small value, the same amount of current flow will cause its voltage to change by a greater amount and the output will be more distorted. Further distortion will take place if R-2 is decreased. This will result in greater current flow through the coupling condenser and a greater change in voltage across it. To improve the low frequency response of an RC-coupled amplifier and thereby reduce the distortion that occurs in the flat portion of the square wave, R-2 and C-1 should be as large as possible.

Distortion of Square Waves (continued)

Even with good low frequency response, there might be a cause for distortion. This cause, as you may have guessed, would be poor high frequency response. This distortion appears in the output as an unfaithful reproduction of the steep portions of the square wave.

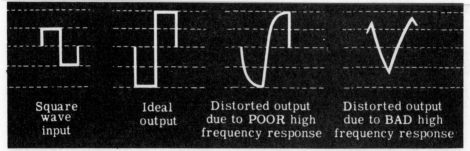

| Square wave input | Ideal output | Distorted output due to POOR high frequency response | Distorted output due to BAD high frequency response |

The stray capacitance, C-2, is the cause of this distortion. It cannot change its voltage instantaneously and, since C-2 is directly across the output, the output voltage cannot change instantaneously either. The stray capacitance, C-2, can charge and discharge through R-1 and R-2 which are in parallel. If the parallel combination of R-1 and R-2 allows C-2 to charge and discharge quickly, the output will show little or no distortion. If R-1 and R-2 are large resistances, C-2 will require a relatively long time to charge and discharge and the steep sides of the square wave will not be perfectly vertical. The larger these resistances become, the worse the distortion becomes. When this becomes very severe, C-2 will never be able to charge and discharge enough to reach the flat portion of the square wave and the output will resemble the triangularly shaped wave shown above.

Stray capacitance due to capacity of tube and wiring

If you recall the discussion about improving the high frequency response of audio amplifiers, you will remember that there are two different ways of doing this. The first is to reduce the stray capacitances C-2 by using special amplifier tubes with very low values of input and output capacitance and by using special wiring techniques to reduce the stray capacitance between the wires and ground. The second way is to reduce the time it takes C-2 to charge and discharge. This is done by using lower values of R-1 and R-2.

As you know, reducing R-2 would harm the low frequency response. Therefore this is not done. Reducing R-1 reduces the gain of the stage but this disadvantage is overcome in video amplifiers by adding more stages, each with low gain but good frequency response. Special tubes are used such as the 6AC7, 6SH7 and the 6AG7. These tubes are designed for high gains and low input and output capacitances and are, therefore, ideally suited for video amplifiers.

Compensating Networks—High-Frequency Compensation

One common way of improving wave shapes in video amplifiers is to decrease the effect of the things which cause distortion. This includes adjusting the values of R and C in the coupling network so as to reduce distortion. You have already seen how this works. Another way is to introduce just the opposite distortion into the circuit by adding compensating networks which counteract the distortion that is already there.

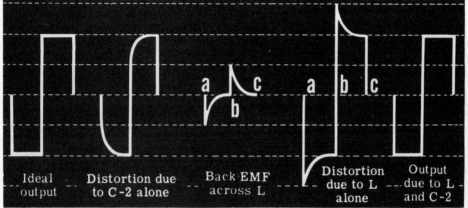

| Ideal output | Distortion due to C-2 alone | Back EMF across L | Distortion due to L alone | Output due to L and C-2 |

To improve the steepness of the steep portion of the square wave, an inductance (L) is placed in series with the plate load resistor (R-1). The back emf set up in this inductance every time the plate current changes will be in such a direction as to cause a peak to appear in the plate voltage.

At (a), the grid voltage is swinging positive and the plate current increases. The plate voltage decreases and at the same instant, a back emf is set up across L. This back emf tends to oppose the increase of current and has the direction shown in the diagram. This negative back emf lowers the plate voltage below its normally low value, thus causing a peak to appear on the square wave.

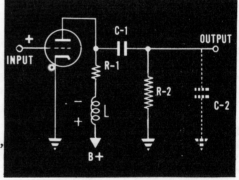

When the grid voltage swings negative, as at (b), the plate current decreases and the back emf across L is in the opposite direction. This then adds to the plate voltage—normally high anyway—causing another peak to appear at (b). Because of the effect of this inductance, it is always referred to as a "peaking coil."

Now consider the effect of these peaks on the charging and discharging of C-2, the stray capacitance. C-2 will now tend to charge to higher values of voltage—higher because of the peaks—and to discharge to lower values of voltage. This will cause C-2 to charge and discharge faster than it would if no peaking coil were used. If the proper value of L is used, the final output can be made an almost perfect square wave.

Compensating Networks—Low-Frequency Compensation

The most common compensating circuit used for correcting low frequency distortion is one that resembles a decoupling network. Like the peaking coil, this circuit introduces a distortion that is opposite, and so counterbalances the distortion due to other causes.

The distortion this circuit compensates for is the distortion of the flat region of the square wave caused by the voltage changes across the coupling condenser. This is how this circuit accomplishes its purpose:

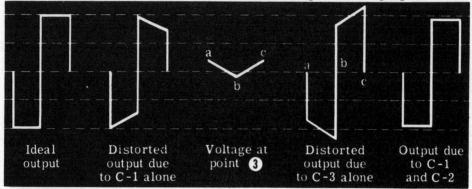

| Ideal output | Distorted output due to C-1 alone | Voltage at point ❸ | Distorted output due to C-3 alone | Output due to C-1 and C-2 |

At (a), the plate current increases, the voltage drop across the R-1 increases, and the voltage drop across R-3 (in the compensating network) tends to increase. The voltage at point 1 in the circuit tends to decrease as a result. The condenser C-3 will discharge and the voltage at point 1 will decrease as the condenser discharges. Thus, the plate voltage will continue to decrease between time (a) and time (b). (Now, the voltage across the coupling condenser can change during this time, and the voltage across the grid resistor R-2 will remain constant.)

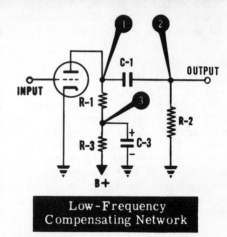

Low-Frequency Compensating Network

At (b), the current suddenly decreases and the voltage at point 1 rises as the condenser C-3 charges up. Thus between time (b) and time (c), the plate voltage is increasing.

Let's see what happens to the flat portion of the square wave in the output. Without the compensating network, the voltage across the coupling condenser changed and this change, subtracted from the steady plate voltage, leaves a distorted voltage across R-2. With the compensating network, the voltage across the coupling condenser still changes, but these changes subtract not from a steady plate voltage but from a plate voltage that is itself changing in an opposite direction. In a properly designed circuit, the voltage across R-2 will be an almost perfect square wave.

Improving Frequency Response—Degeneration

If there were no compensating circuits used, distortion would appear in the output. Let's say that a perfect square wave (wave form 1) is connected to the grid of an amplifier, and that the output is distorted as shown in wave form 2.

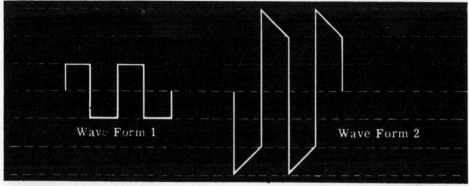

Wave Form 1   Wave Form 2

Now let's take a small part of the output wave form (as in wave form 3) and bring it back to the input. The resulting input would be the sum of the original input and this voltage which is fed back from the output. The new input will look like wave form 4.

Wave Form 3   Wave Form 4

The new voltage at the plate of the amplifier will be wave form 5 which, you will notice, has just the opposite distortion than existed when the input was a perfect square wave. Whatever was causing distortion before is still causing it now, with the result that the output is still distorted but not nearly so much as it was previously. Compare wave form 6 (the new output) with wave form 2 (the old output).

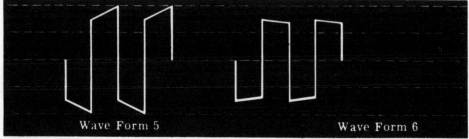

Wave Form 5   Wave Form 6

You will notice that the new input wave form (no. 4) is smaller than wave form 1, the old input. This is so because the voltage that was fed back is out of phase with, and so subtracts from, the original signal input. Thus the output is smaller than it would ordinarily be and the gain of the stage is apparently lessened. More important than the loss of gain is the decrease in the amount of distortion. This method of decreasing distortion is known as "degeneration" or as "negative feedback."

Improving Frequency Response—Degeneration (continued)

There are several ways of obtaining negative feedback. One of the simplest and most widely used methods is to have the cathode bias resistor, R-4, unbypassed. In this way the cathode voltage will not be pure DC but will vary as the current varies. When the grid goes positive (or less negative), the cathode current increases and the cathode voltage goes positive. This cathode voltage decreases the grid-to-cathode signal and so lowers the gain of the stage. Furthermore, the cathode current will not be of the same wave shape as the grid voltage if distortion is present in the circuit. The cathode voltage will contain this distortion and the difference between the grid and the cathode voltages will contain just the opposite distortion. This reduces the distortion in the output.

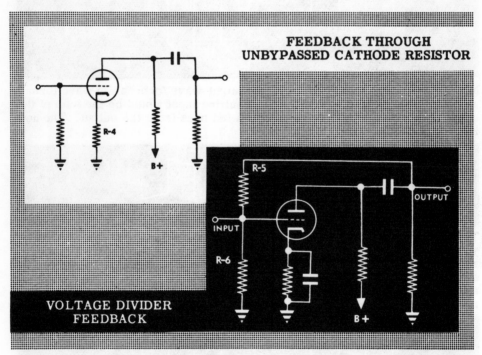

FEEDBACK THROUGH
UNBYPASSED CATHODE RESISTOR

VOLTAGE DIVIDER
FEEDBACK

Another way of obtaining negative feedback is to use a voltage divider consisting of R-6, the grid resistor, and R-5. This voltage divider is connected across the output so that part of the output voltage appears across R-6. In addition, the input signal appears across R-6. Since the output and input signals are 180 degrees out of phase, the resultant input signal to the grid will be the difference between the input to the stage and that part of the output signal that is fed back. This, of course, will counteract part of the distortion in the output.

In each of these two circuits, it is possible to adjust the amount of signal that is fed back. If the unbypassed cathode resistor, R-4, is increased or, in the other circuit, if R-5 is decreased the feedback will be increased. Increasing the feedback lowers the gain of the stage and makes the output signal resemble the input signal more closely.

Improving Frequency Response—Degeneration (continued)

Degeneration works equally well for all types of distortion. In the illustrations shown on the previous sheet, you saw how degeneration improves the response of the amplifier to the flat portion of the square wave. Below, you see the six wave forms that explain how degeneration improves the steepness of the steep portion of the square wave. As before, wave form 1 is the original input to the grid; wave form 2 is the signal that would appear in the output if no negative feedback were used; wave form 3 is the part of output signal that is fed back and appears between grid and cathode; wave form 4 is the resultant grid-to-cathode signal; wave form 5 is the amplified resultant grid voltage as it appears on the plate; and wave form 6 is the new output voltage—reduced in height but with much less distortion than wave form 2.

Wave Form 1	Wave Form 2	Wave Form 3	Wave Form 4	Wave Form 5	Wave Form 6

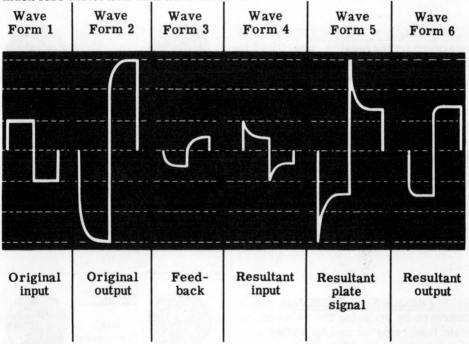

Original input	Original output	Feed-back	Resultant input	Resultant plate signal	Resultant output

The important thing to remember is that the signal which is fed back contains the distortion that exists in the output. When this signal is combined with the original grid signal, the distortion appears "backward." The resulting plate signal has distortion that is opposite to the distortion originally existing in the output. In this respect, negative feedback does almost the same thing as a compensating network. The important differences are these:

1. Negative feedback will reduce any type of distortion while a compensating network will work only for the type of distortion it is designed to eliminate.

2. Negative feedback will always result in decreased gain.

Review of Video Amplifiers

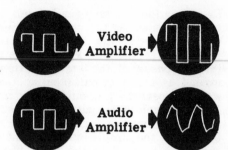

VIDEO AMPLIFIER amplifies pulses, triangular or square waves, without distortion, whereas an audio amplifier distorts these wave forms due to poor high and low frequency response.

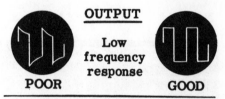

LOW FREQUENCY RESPONSE can be improved by increasing capacity of the coupling capacitor and by adding a low frequency compensating network.

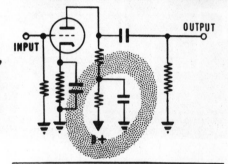

LOW FREQUENCY COMPENSATING NETWORK develops a varying voltage, which, when added to the square wave input voltage, counteracts the distortion of flat portion of square wave due to the coupling capacitor.

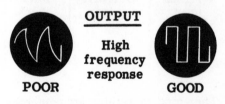

HIGH FREQUENCY RESPONSE can be improved by reducing the value of the plate load resistor and by adding a peaking coil in the plate lead.

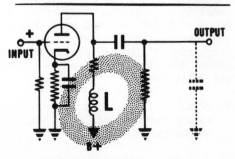

PEAKING COIL counteracts the effect of stray capacitance, which tends to round off the leading edge of the square wave.

Review of Video Amplifiers (continued)

DEGENERATION or negative feedback is a method of overcoming any type of square wave distortion by returning part of output as a grid signal. Resultant output contains very little distortion.

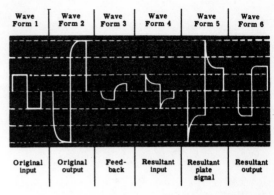

Wave Form 1	Wave Form 2	Wave Form 3	Wave Form 4	Wave Form 5	Wave Form 6
Original input	Original output	Feed-back	Resultant input	Resultant plate signal	Resultant output

UNBYPASSED CATHODE RESISTOR provides degeneration by forcing the cathode voltage to vary as the current varies, introducing distortion opposite to, and thus reducing, that present.

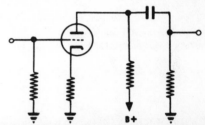

VOLTAGE DIVIDER FEED-BACK introduces part of the output voltage across the grid but 180 degrees out of phase, so that distortion is introduced in reverse and thus reduced.

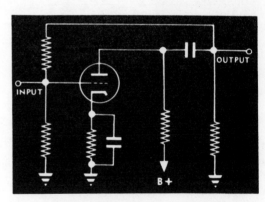

VIDEO AMPLIFIER CIRCUIT may contain all or several of the distortion-reducing components.

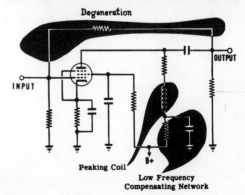

Degeneration

OUTPUT

INPUT

B+

Peaking Coil

Low Frequency Compensating Network

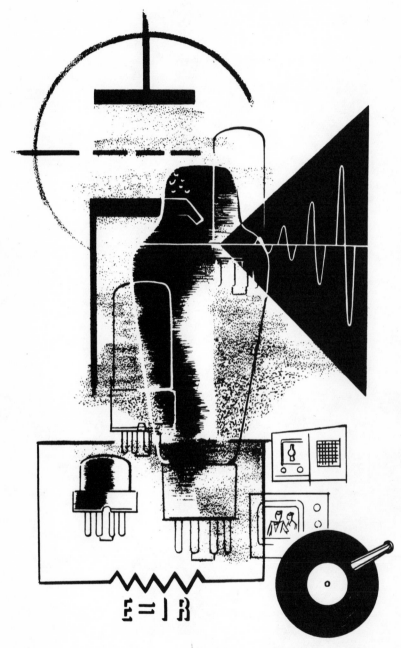

E = I R

RF *Amplifiers*

Amplifiers and Amplification

In order to understand what an RF amplifier is, you ought to review amplifiers and amplification. An amplifier is an electronic device which uses vacuum tubes to build up an AC voltage. Suppose you need 10 volts to drive a pair of headphones or a loudspeaker and the signal voltage is only 0.1 volts, which is too small to be used. This signal is fed into the grid of an amplifier tube which builds it up to 1.0 volts. Then you feed the 1.0 volt into another amplifier tube and it gives 10 volts output.

You have the alternative of using one amplifier tube with a gain of 100 and building up the voltage to 10 volts in one step. When two tubes are used to do the job, it is called a two-stage amplifier. When one is used, it is a single-stage amplifier. Some amplifiers use as many as 5 stages to build up a voltage large enough to drive a piece of equipment.

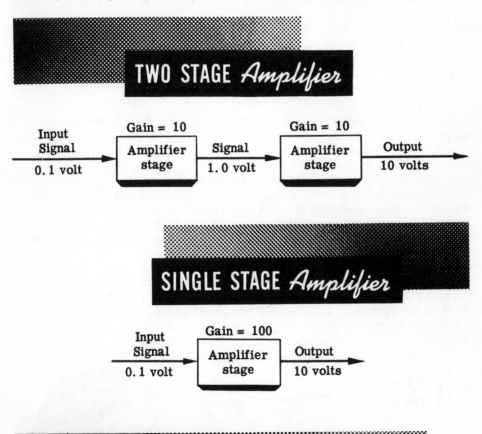

When an amplifier builds up the voltage 10 times, it has a voltage gain of 10. The voltage gain is the number of times a stage or group of stages amplifies the signal.

INTRODUCTION TO THE RF AMPLIFIER

What an RF Amplifier Does

Now you are ready to examine what makes an RF amplifier different from other types of amplifiers. You remember that:

1. Audio amplifiers amplify all frequencies from about 15 to 15,000 cycles per second.

2. Video amplifiers amplify all frequencies from about 30 to 6,000,000 cycles per second.

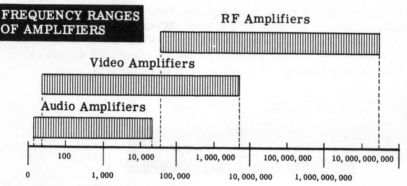

RF amplifiers amplify signals from about 30,000 to 30,000,000,000 cycles per second. The outstanding feature of an RF amplifier is that it does not amplify this entire frequency range at once. It selects one small portion—the portion occupied by the radio signal sent out by one transmitter—and amplifies that. For instance, WCBS broadcasts at a frequency of 880 kilocycles and is allotted a band whose limits are 5 kilocycles either side of 880. Most standard broadcast stations are allotted a band 5 kc either side of a center frequency. When you tune a broadcast receiver to WCBS you are adjusting the RF amplifier to select the band of frequencies extending from 875 to 885 kc.

The same principle applies to short wave and television stations. For example, a station at 10 mc might have a bandwidth from 9.8 to 10.2 mc. A perfect RF amplifier would select that range of frequencies and reject all others. Television channel 2 occupies the band from 54 to 60 mc. When you tune a television set to channel 2 you are adjusting the RF amplifier to select that band and reject all others.

What an RF Amplifier Does (continued)

You already know that a signal sent out by a radio transmitter travels through the air to reach your radio, sometimes for thousands of miles. The transmitter may be putting out thousands of watts of power, but when the signal reaches your receiver it may be very weak. The signal coming into your receiver is usually in the order of a few millionths of a volt and must be amplified many times before it will drive a loud-speaker or earphones.

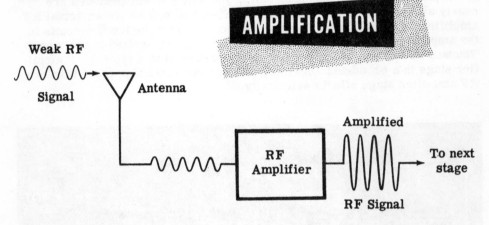

It is possible to amplify a radio signal in several different ways. You may amplify it at radio frequency as it comes from the antenna, or you may convert it to lower radio frequencies or even audio frequency and then amplify it. These various methods will be discussed later in Volume 5 under Radio Receivers. The important point is that amplification is not the only function of an RF amplifier. The most important thing an RF amplifier does is to separate the stations whose signals reach the radio receiver. This process is called "tuning." When you tune a receiver or a transmitter or a radar unit, you are changing the frequency to which the RF amplifier is set.

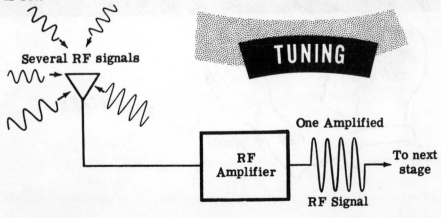

This Is What You Will Learn about RF Amplifiers

Before you learn more about RF amplifiers, you will have a brief review of resonance. In addition to what you learned about coils and capacitors in Basic Electricity, you will be shown how the resonant effect is used to tune an RF amplifier stage. The selectivity of tuned circuits and "Q" will be explained and you will be shown the construction of antenna and RF coils actually in use.

After the section on resonant circuits, you will see why pentodes are nearly always used as RF amplifiers. Then you will be shown actual RF amplifier circuits illustrating how you may connect the tuned circuits to the amplifier tube and how the correct voltages are applied to the tube. You will go through an analysis of every part used in a typical RF amplifier stage in a broadcast receiver, and find out how using more than one RF amplifier stage affects selectivity.

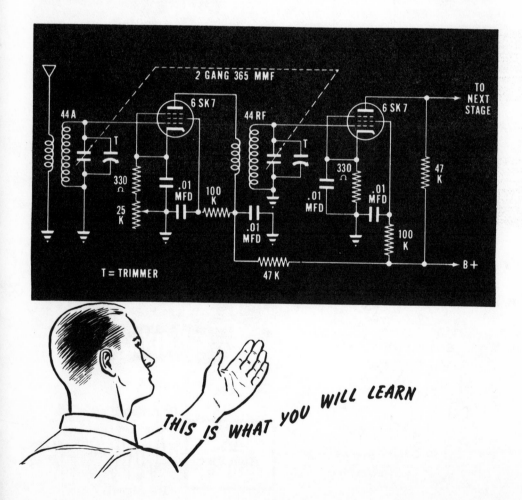

What a Tuned Circuit Is

From the introduction to RF amplifiers, you learned that all RF amplifiers perform two important functions:

1. They amplify the signal at radio frequencies.
2. They select one narrow band of frequencies and reject all others.

Amplification of the signal is accomplished by a vacuum tube, just as in audio and video amplifiers. You have already learned just about all you need to know about amplification.

The job of selecting one narrow band of frequencies to be amplified is performed by the RF amplifier's "tuned circuit." The tuned circuit consists of coils and capacitors connected to form a resonant LC circuit, which is "tuned" to the desired frequency. On the following sheets you will see how tuned circuits work in RF amplifiers.

Review of Series LC Circuits

In a radio receiver there are many signals of different frequencies coming into the antenna. The listener tunes the radio by adjusting the tuning capacitor. This makes the antenna coil and capacitor resonate to the frequency of the desired station. Because of the resonant effect, the coil and capacitor select only that signal tuned to their resonant frequency. In order to understand exactly what the resonant effect is, let's review series LC circuits and then parallel LC circuits.

You remember that a coil offers less opposition to low frequencies than to high ones. A capacitor offers less opposition to high frequencies than to low ones. This opposition is called reactance.

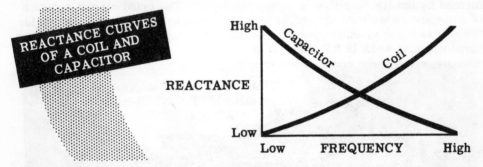

REACTANCE CURVES OF A COIL AND CAPACITOR

In the series LC circuit shown below, assume that the signal generator is delivering a very low frequency. The coil will offer little opposition to this low frequency, but the capacitor will offer very high opposition. Therefore very little current will flow, because the total reactance of the circuit is high. On the other hand, if the signal generator delivers a very high frequency, the coil will offer very high opposition, and the current will still be low. At some intermediate frequency the reactance of the coil will equal the reactance of the capacitor. At this frequency (the resonant frequency), the impedance of the circuit will be minimum and the current will be maximum.

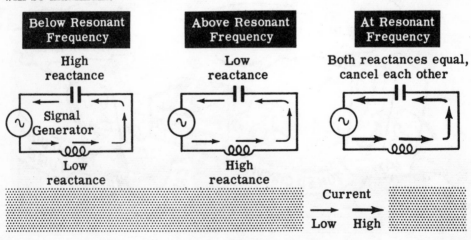

Review of Parallel LC Circuits

Most radio receivers employ parallel-resonant rather than series-resonant circuits for tuning to different frequencies.

The reactance of coils and capacitors varies with the frequency applied to them, as you saw on the previous sheet. In addition to this, coils and capacitors have another property which is important in resonant circuits. A coil causes the current to lag behind the applied voltage by 90 degrees. A capacitor causes the current to lead the applied voltage by 90 degrees.

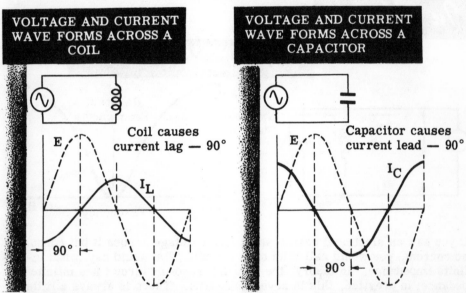

VOLTAGE AND CURRENT WAVE FORMS ACROSS A COIL

Coil causes current lag — 90°

E

I_L

90°

VOLTAGE AND CURRENT WAVE FORMS ACROSS A CAPACITOR

Capacitor causes current lead — 90°

E

I_C

90°

If you connect a coil in parallel with a capacitor, the current in the coil is 90 degrees behind the applied voltage plus 90 degrees behind the current in the capacitor, or, a total of 180 degrees out of phase with the capacitor current. You remember from Basic Electricity that currents which are 180 degrees out of phase cancel one another. If the capacitor alone draws 3 amps and the coil alone draws 2 amps, then the combination of the two will draw 3 -2 or 1 amp.

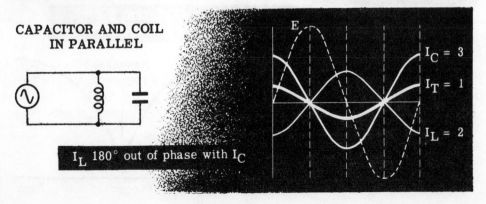

CAPACITOR AND COIL IN PARALLEL

E

$I_C = 3$

$I_T = 1$

$I_L = 2$

I_L 180° out of phase with I_C

Review of Parallel LC Circuits (continued)

Since the coil and capacitor are in parallel, the voltage across them is the same. If you choose a frequency at which the reactance of the coil equals the reactance of the capacitor and feed this frequency into them, the current in the coil will be equal and opposite to the current in the capacitor. Then no current will flow through the combination of the two. The frequency at which this occurs is called the resonant frequency, and it is at this frequency that the tuned circuit's impedance is greatest.

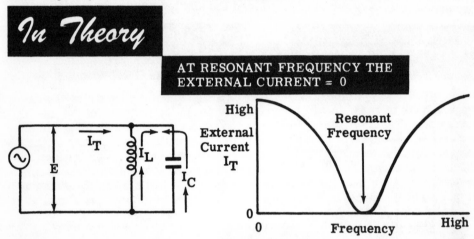

In Theory

AT RESONANT FREQUENCY THE EXTERNAL CURRENT = 0

If you saw an electrical device which had a voltage across it but conducted no current, you would call it an open circuit. You would say it had infinite impedance. In theory, the parallel-resonant circuit has infinite impedance; in practice, this is never quite true. There is always a little current flowing in the external circuit, even at the resonant point. This is because all real coils have some resistance. As a result, the current in the coil is not quite 180 degrees out of phase with the current in the capacitor, and they don't cancel each other out completely.

In Practice

AT RESONANT FREQUENCY THE EXTERNAL CURRENT IS MINIMUM

How the Resonant Circuit Selects Stations

So far you know that a parallel tuned circuit has a very high impedance at the resonant frequency and a low impedance at all other frequencies. If you understand this, it will be easy to see how a parallel LC circuit selects stations.

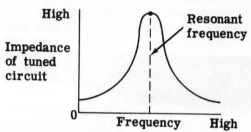

PARALLEL TUNED CIRCUIT—HIGH IMPEDANCE ONLY AT RESONANT FREQUENCY

In the circuit shown below, signals of different frequencies strike the antenna. Each of them starts a current flowing in the primary of the antenna coil. Each of these currents in the primary induces a voltage in the secondary. A variable capacitor is in parallel with the secondary of the antenna coil. A parallel LC circuit has a low impedance to all frequencies except its resonant frequency. Therefore it short-circuits signals at all frequencies other than its resonant frequency. It has a high impedance at its resonant frequency. Therefore it does not short-circuit the signal at this frequency, but allows it to build up.

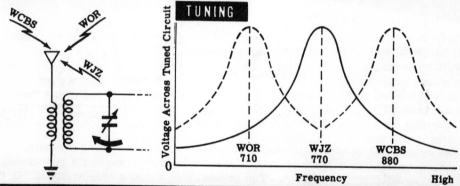

Changing Capacitor Setting—Changes Circuit's Resonant Frequency

One particular coil and one particular capacitor will resonate to one frequency only. Varying either the inductance or the capacitance of the tuned circuit will change the resonant frequency. In the process of tuning, you can change the capacitance of the tuned circuit by using a variable capacitor. When the resonant frequency of the LC circuit coincides with the frequency of some signal, you have tuned the RF amplifier to that signal.

Naturally no tuning system is perfect. Signals whose frequencies are very close to each other will all get to the loudspeaker. Then the one to which the receiver tunes will be only a little louder than the others. Signals of exactly the same frequency will certainly get to the loudspeaker together. Then, the strongest signal will be heard the loudest.

"Q" and Selectivity

In audio and video amplifiers, it is desirable to have the amplification stage pass a wide range of frequencies. On the other hand, in RF amplifiers we would like the amplification stage to select a narrow band of frequencies and reject the rest. Only then can it separate stations which are close together on the dial. The narrower a band of frequencies passed by an amplifier, the greater is its selectivity. Thus selectivity is the ability of an amplifier to select one of many signals which are close in frequency.

The selectivity of an RF amplifier is determined by its tuned circuits. The lower we can make a coil's resistance in proportion to its reactance, the more selective it will be. The measure of a coil's selectivity is "Q," which is equal to its reactance divided by its resistance. Since the resistance of a capacitor is lower than that of a coil, the coil is the weakest link in a tuned circuit. The Q of the tuned circuit is the Q of the coil.

$$Q = \frac{\text{REACTANCE OF COIL}}{\text{RESISTANCE OF COIL}} = \frac{X_L}{R_L}$$

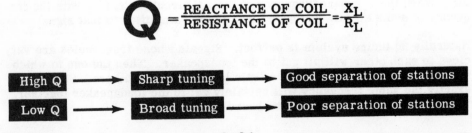

How Tuning Capacitors Are Constructed

In Basic Electricity you were shown the construction of the two types of capacitors, fixed and variable. Variable capacitors are used in tuned circuits so that you can vary their capacitance and thus change the frequency. Variable capacitors have one set of plates called the rotors which can be rotated in and out of another set of fixed plates called the stators The dielectric is air. As the rotor plates are rotated farther and farther out of the stators, the capacity of the unit decreases.

Most radio receivers with RF amplifiers employ more than one tuned circuit. Each tuned circuit needs a variable capacitor. If you mounted each variable capacitor separately, you would have to tune each one separately and this would be inconvenient. Instead, you can mount the rotors of several identical variable capacitors on a single shaft. This is called "ganging" them. When one rotor is turned, the others turn the same amount.

ONE-GANG CAPACITOR

TWO-GANG CAPACITOR

Ganged capacitors involve one big difficulty. Although each of the ganged units measures the same size and has the same spacing, there are small differences in capacity between the units. This is because it is economically impractical to manufacture any two things which are exactly the same size. To compensate for the differences in capacity, a small variable capacitor is connected in parallel with each variable capacitor unit to be ganged. Each of these small compensating capacitors can be adjusted separately until all of the gangs have the same capacity. These compensating capacitors are called "trimmers" because their capacitance is used to trim the capacitance of the main tuning units.

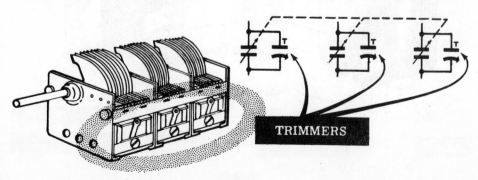

TRIMMERS

How Tuning Coils Are Constructed

Many tuned RF coils are really transformers and have two windings—the primary and secondary. The coils are wound on a bakelite or cardboard form and generally have an air core, although low frequency coils may occasionally have a powdered iron core.

In order to prevent stray electric fields from affecting the action of RF coils, shields are generally placed around the coils. These shields alter the the inductance of the coil. Therefore any receiver adjustments, such as the alignment process which will be described shortly, should be performed with the shields in place.

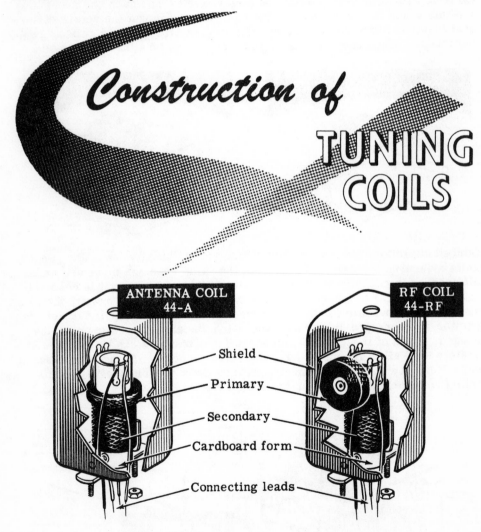

Review of Tuned Circuits

In this topic you have studied the action of a resonant circuit and how resonant circuits are used to tune RF amplifiers and radio receivers in general. There are several main points you should understand thoroughly in order to apply what you have learned.

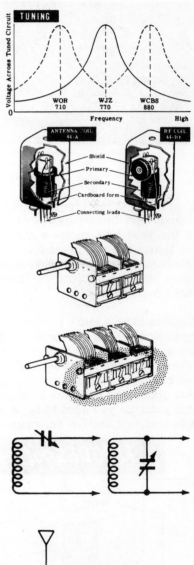

TUNING—Selecting a signal at one frequency and rejecting signals at all other frequencies. This is done by a coil and capacitor.

RF COILS—Generally have primary and secondary windings. The secondary is usually tuned. Most of them come with shield cans.

TUNING CAPACITORS—These are variable air capacitors. Several air capacitors may be ganged into one unit.

TRIMMERS—Are small capacitors placed in parallel with each unit of a ganged capacitor. Their function is to compensate for small differences in capacity between the units.

RESONANT CIRCUIT—A circuit in which a capacitor and a coil are connected in series or in parallel. Its function is to tune.

PARALLEL RESONANT CIRCUIT—The tuning capacitor is connected in parallel with the coil. It has high impedance at the resonant frequency and low impedance at all other frequencies. It builds up a high voltage at the resonant frequency and a low voltage at all other frequencies. This type of circuit is used most often to tune radio receivers.

Why the Pentode is Used in RF Amplifiers

You have just studied the operation of the tuned circuits in an RF amplifier. Now you are ready to begin work on the amplifier tube itself. The first question is—what kind of amplifier tube will do the job best?

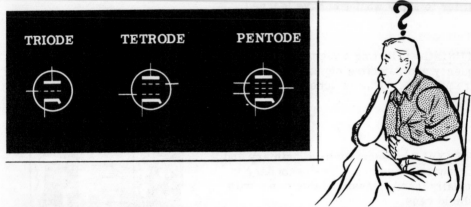

There are three types of tubes which might be used—the triode, the tetrode and the pentode. At first glance it might seem that the triode is the best tube to use since it is the simplest of the three. However, the triode has two great disadvantages when used as an RF amplifier—no triode has an amplification factor of over 100. Tetrodes and pentodes have much higher amplification factors and therefore are capable of amplifying many more times.

Triodes have a much higher capacitance from grid to plate than tetrodes or pentodes. An RF amplifier generally has tuned circuits in both its input and its output and these tuned circuits resonate to the same frequency. When you learn about oscillators you will find out that a triode whose output and input circuits are tuned to the same frequency tends to generate its own signal, or oscillate because of the high grid to plate capacitance. At this point all you need to know is that a triode used as an RF amplifier will tend to make the entire receiver howl.

Why the Pentode is Used in RF Amplifiers (continued)

By now it ought to be obvious that a triode is not well suited for use as an RF amplifier. A tube with a screen grid should clear up the difficulties which are encountered when a triode is used. This leaves a choice between the tetrode and the pentode.

Tetrodes do not oscillate because the screen grid cuts down the capacity between the control grid and the plate. They do have two drawbacks, however, that are not present in the pentode. Tetrodes do not have an amplification factor of over several hundred, while pentodes have an amplification factor up to several thousand. Therefore pentodes are preferable. Also, the tetrode produces secondary emission. Electrons from the cathode hit the plate at high velocities. Some of them bounce off of the plate and are attracted to the screen grid which is at a positive potential. This cuts down the plate current and causes distortion. Secondary emission is not present in the triode because it has no screen grid. Pentodes do not have this difficulty for a different reason.

Pentodes have a third grid which is placed between the screen grid and the plate. This is the suppressor grid put there for the sole purpose of cutting down secondary emission. This is how it works. Electrons which bounce off the plate might drift back to the screen grid if the suppressor grid were not there to stop them. The suppressor grid is connected to the cathode or to ground and has an excess of electrons just like the cathode. Therefore the electrons which bounce off the plate are repelled back to the plate by the suppressor grid, and secondary emission is virtually eliminated.

A SINGLE-STAGE RF AMPLIFIER

How the Coils and Capacitors are Connected to the Tube

You can connect coils and capacitors in two possible ways to make them tune to a given frequency—in series or in parallel. Almost all RF amplifiers employ parallel tuned circuits. The most common method of arranging tuned circuits in an RF amplifier, and the one you will use, is shown below.

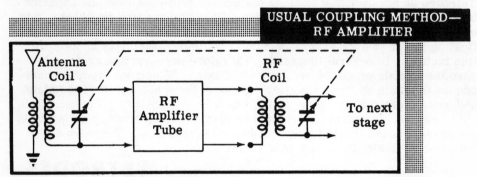

However, this is not the only type of circuit which can be used to tune an RF amplifier. You may occasionally find other circuit arrangements. Either the input circuit or the output circuit may be altered and still produce a practical tuning arrangement. Here are some other ways.

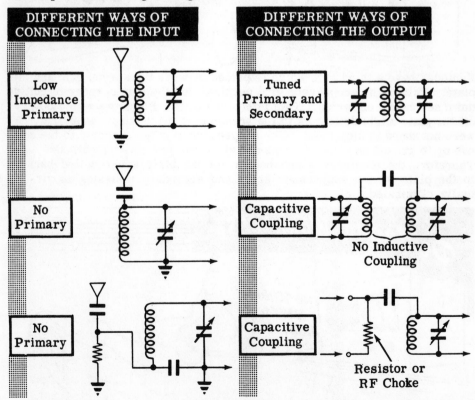

A SINGLE-STAGE RF AMPLIFIER

The Development of the RF Amplifier Circuit

You remember from the sections on vacuum tube theory that the function of a grid is to permit amplification of a signal. The signal to be amplified is fed into the grid and the output of the tube is taken from a load impedance in the plate circuit. You know how pentodes operate, and you know how tuned circuits operate. Now put them together, and this is what you have.

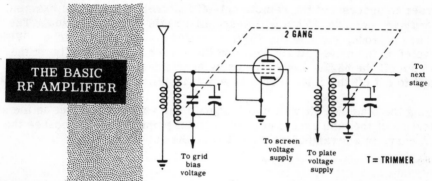

There are only a few differences between the above circuit and circuits actually used in radio receivers. First of all, separate power supplies are seldom used for the plate and screen voltages. The plate voltage supply is generally lowered by a dropping resistor or a voltage divider to supply voltage to the screen (see R-2 in diagram below). Also the voltage on the screen should not be allowed to vary up and down with changes in the signal, or distortion will result. For this reason the screen needs its own bypass capacitor (C-6).

Secondly, grid bias voltage is seldom taken from an outside source. Instead it is generated by the tube itself, using a method which should be familiar to you—cathode bias (R-1). The cathode bias resistor is bypassed to prevent degeneration (C-5).

Very often in multi-stage RF amplifiers a decoupling filter (C-7 and R-3) is placed in the plate supply to prevent one stage from interacting with the next. It is a good policy to use a decoupling filter even in a single-stage RF amplifier.

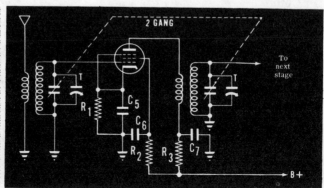

The Remote Cut-off Pentode

If you look up the 6SK7 in the tube manual, you'll find it is called a "remote cut-off" pentode. In other places it is called a "variable mu" pentode and a "super control" tube. The first two titles actually describe an important feature of this tube. The third title describes nothing and is just a name.

In order to understand the remote cut-off feature, suppose you examine the ordinary pentode. This will serve as a basis for comparison. The ordinary pentode, such as the 6SJ7, is called a "sharp cut-off" tube. With 250 volts on the plate and 100 volts on the screen, minus 9 volts on the grid cuts off the 6SJ7. Under the same conditions, minus 35 volts are needed to cut off the 6SK7. This is why it is called a "remote cut-off" tube.

Varying the bias of a sharp cut-off pentode has very little effect on the amplification of the tube except near the cut-off point. This is because the E_g-I_p curve is a straight line except near the cut-off point.

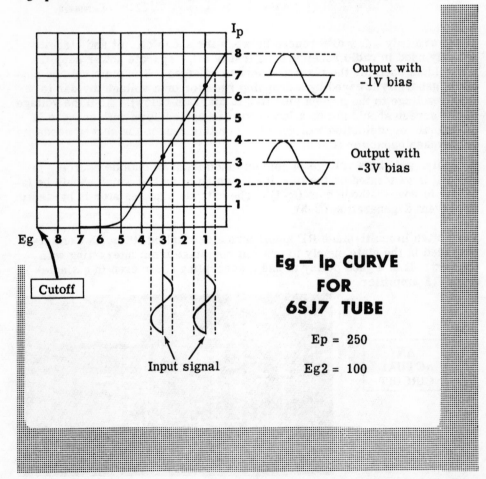

Eg – Ip CURVE FOR 6SJ7 TUBE

Ep = 250

Eg2 = 100

The Remote Cut-off Pentode (continued)

Varying the bias of a remote cut-off pentode varies the amplification. To understand this, look at the Eg-Ip graph of the 6SK7. The graph shows a 1-volt signal applied to the grid of a 6SK7 under two different conditions: (1) when the bias is -1 volt and (2) when the bias is -9 volts. Notice that the plate current variation is five times as large in the first case as it is in the second case. Therefore the amplification varies with the bias. This is why the 6SK7 is called a "variable mu pentode."

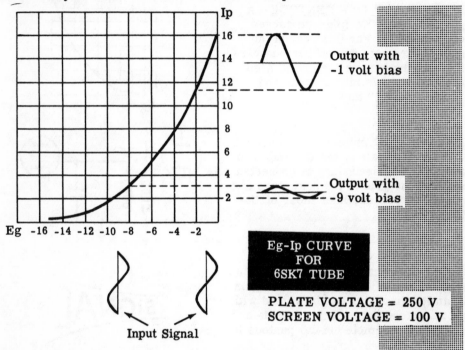

Input Signal

Eg-Ip CURVE
FOR
6SK7 TUBE

PLATE VOLTAGE = 250 V
SCREEN VOLTAGE = 100 V

In a remote cut-off pentode the turns of the control grid are spaced closely at the edges and farther apart at the center. The electron flow through the edges of the grid is cut off by very little negative bias. However the electron flow through the center of the grid can only be cut off by a high negative bias. The grid of a sharp cut-off pentode is uniformly spaced. The entire plate current is cut off by one value of bias.

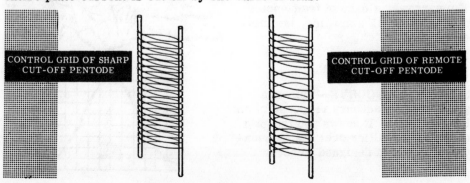

CONTROL GRID OF SHARP CUT-OFF PENTODE

CONTROL GRID OF REMOTE CUT-OFF PENTODE

A SINGLE-STAGE RF AMPLIFIER

Review of the Single-Stage RF Amplifier

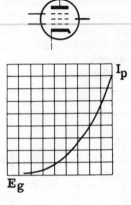

PENTODE—A tube used almost uni-versally as an RF amplifier, because it has the highest gain, least tendency to oscillate, and least distortion.

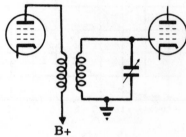

REMOTE CUT-OFF PENTODE—A pentode whose Eg-Ip graph curves continuously. For this reason the gain of a remote cut-off pentode var-ies with the bias on the grid. Also called "variable mu" pentode and "super control" tube.

RF COIL—The primary is connected between the plate of the RF amplifier and B+. The secondary is connected between the grid of the next stage and ground. Also shielded most of the time.

GAIN—The number of times a tube or RF coil amplifies a signal. The gain of an RF amplifier can be varied with a pot. placed between the cathode and ground (if a remote cut-off pentode is used).

SELECTIVITY—Is the ability of an RF amplifier to separate signals whose frequencies are close together. The narrower a band of frequencies passed by an RF amplifier, the more selective it is.

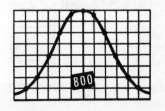

SELECTIVITY CURVE—This is a graph of the frequency response of an RF amplifier. It shows you the gain of the RF amplifier over the frequen-cies which it is designed to cover.

THE TWO-STAGE RF AMPLIFIER

Why More Than One RF Stage Is Used

You remember from the previous topic that an **RF amplifier** performs two functions:

1. It amplifies an RF signal.
2. It selects a frequency.

When a receiver is close to a transmitter, the signal picked up by the receiver is strong. Such receivers probably need only one RF amplifier stage. On the other hand, some receivers are designed to pick up signals from transmitters several thousand miles away and by the time this signal reaches the receiver, it is very weak; the receiver needs extra amplification to boost it. Such receivers require more than one RF amplifier stage.

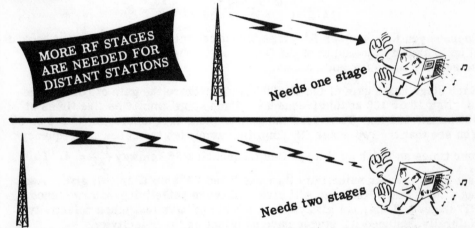

MORE RF STAGES ARE NEEDED FOR DISTANT STATIONS

Needs one stage

Needs two stages

There is a second, and less obvious, reason for using more than one RF stage. More than one RF amplifier stage gives greater selectivity. More selectivity permits a receiver to separate stations whose frequencies are very close together. There are radio frequency bands in which many stations are crowded into a few megacycles. Receivers designed to cover these bands need more selectivity than one tuned RF amplifier can give them.

? ? ? ?
W2XXX-3.562KC
W5YYY-3.570KC

MORE RF STAGES ARE NEEDED WHERE SIGNAL FREQUENCIES ARE CLOSE TOGETHER

THE TWO-STAGE RF AMPLIFIER

Why More Than One RF Stage Is Used (continued)

In order to understand how more RF stages give better selectivity, suppose you examine a typical selectivity curve more carefully. Figure 1 is a curve for a single stage RF amplifier tuned to 500 kc. 10 microvolts of RF are fed into the amplifier.

You will notice that the output of the amplifier at 500 kc is 100 microvolts. Therefore the gain at 500 kc is: $\dfrac{\text{OUTPUT}}{\text{INPUT}} = \dfrac{100}{10} = 10.$

The output at 465 kc and 535 kc is 50 microvolts.

Therefore the gain at these frequencies is $\dfrac{50}{10} = 5.$

The single-stage amplifier amplifies the resonant frequency twice as much as frequencies 35 kc away:

$$\frac{\text{GAIN at 500 kc}}{\text{GAIN at 465 kc or 535 kc}} = \frac{10}{5} = 2.$$

Suppose you took another RF stage, identical with the first one, and hooked it up to amplify the output of the first stage. Figure 2 shows the overall selectivity curve for both stages.

Each stage has a gain of ten at 500 kc. Therefore the gain of both stages is: 10 x 10 or 100 at this frequency. Each stage amplifies five times at 465 kc and 535 kc. Therefore the gain at these frequencies is: 5 x 5 or 25. You see that the two-stage RF amplifier amplifies the resonant frequency four times as much as it amplifies frequencies 35 kc away $\dfrac{100}{25} = 4.$ This is a much greater selectivity than one tuned RF amplifier will give. Adding a third tuned RF stage will give still more selectivity than two tuned RF stages. It may not always be desirable to have that much selectivity. Naturally, untuned RF stages have no effect on the selectivity.

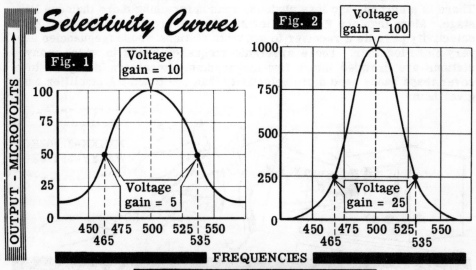

Selectivity Curves

Fig. 1 — Voltage gain = 10 — Voltage gain = 5

Fig. 2 — Voltage gain = 100 — Voltage gain = 25

OUTPUT - MICROVOLTS

FREQUENCIES

INPUT VOLTAGE = 10-MICROVOLTS

Selectivity and Bandpass

There is another idea, related to selectivity, which you ought to understand. This is the idea of "bandpass." The word itself gives you some hint of what it means. It refers to the width of the frequency band passed by an amplifier. Most of the time it is used in connection with RF amplifiers.

BANDPASS - The width of the band of frequencies which is passed by an amplifier between the two points on the selectivity curve where the output is seven-tenths of the output at the resonant frequency.

This is the exact definition of bandpass, but it's a complicated one. You may get a better understanding if you examine an actual selectivity curve and calculate the bandpass. Here is the selectivity curve of a single stage RF amplifier taken from the previous sheet.

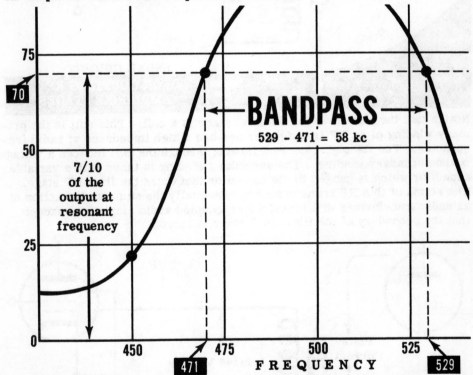

The output of the stage at the resonant frequency is 100 microvolts. Seventenths of this is 70 microvolts. The amplifier stage puts out 70 microvolts at 471 kc and at 529 kc. 529 kc minus 471 kc equals 58 kc. The bandpass of this particular RF amplifier is 58 kc. Now read the definition of bandpass again.

The greater the selectivity, the narrower the bandpass. Calculate the bandpass for the two-stage RF amplifier described on the previous sheet.

How RF Stages Are Coupled

Although you probably know already how one RF amplifier stage is coupled to the next, it might be good to review it at this point. There are several possible ways of coupling two RF stages. The most commonly used method is shown in the illustration below.

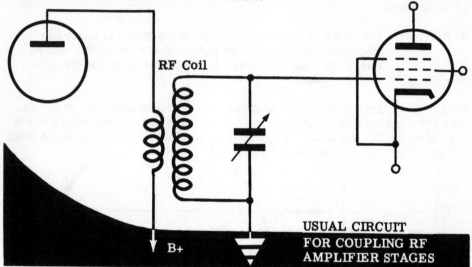

RF Coil

B+

USUAL CIRCUIT
FOR COUPLING RF
AMPLIFIER STAGES

Notice that the plate load for the first stage is a coil. This coil is the primary winding of an RF transformer and has a high impedance at radio frequencies. The RF signal current flowing through the coil induces a voltage in the secondary winding. The secondary winding is tuned with a variable capacitor which is ganged to the capacitor that tunes the first RF stage. The action of this RF transformer is essentially the same as the action of an audio transformer in a transformer-coupled audio amplifier, except that the secondary of the RF transformer is tuned.

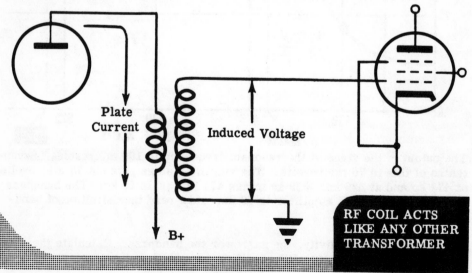

Plate
Current

Induced Voltage

B+

RF COIL ACTS
LIKE ANY OTHER
TRANSFORMER

Review of the Two-Stage RF Amplifier

<u>TWO-STAGE RF AMPLIFIER</u> — When correctly adjusted, it gives more amplification and more selectivity than a single-stage RF amplifier.

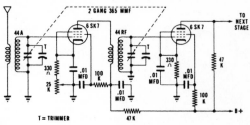

<u>BANDPASS</u> — The width of the band passed by an amplifier between the two points where the output is seven-tenths of the output at the resonant frequency. The greater the selectivity, the narrower the bandpass. The greater the bandpass, the poorer the selectivity.

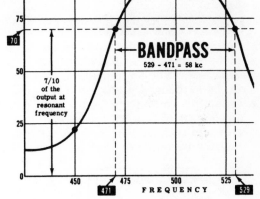

<u>ALIGNMENT</u> — The process of adjusting trimmers in a group of tuned amplifier stages so that all the stages tune to the same frequency. When a multiple-stage RF amplifier is correctly aligned, it will give more selectivity than a single-stage amplifier. When it is not correctly aligned, it may give far less selectivity or even tune to two frequencies at once.

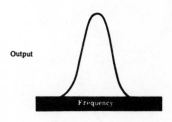

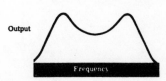

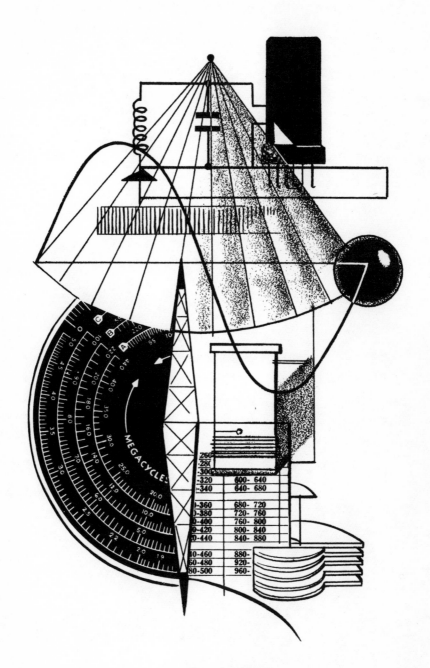

MEGACYCLES

260-		
280		
300-		
-320	600- 640	
-340	640- 680	
-360	680- 720	
-380	720- 760	
-400	760- 800	
-420	800- 840	
-440	840- 880	
-460	880-	
-480	920-	
-500	960-	

Oscillators

Why You Study Oscillators

You have studied how amplifiers function in electronic circuits. No less important are oscillator circuits, or, simply, oscillators. Most modern radio receivers which you have used in your home and in your automobile contain oscillators. Every transmitter that sends intelligence through the air employs an oscillator to produce these signals. This is not only true of "ground stations" like WNBC or WCBS; it applies to every transmitter on a ship or plane. Inter-ship and plane-to-ship communications would be greatly limited if oscillator circuits were not employed.

Oscillators are not used exclusively in communications equipment. The test equipment you use—signal generators and frequency meters—contain oscillator circuits. You will find oscillators in radar and sonar equipment, as well as in certain guided missiles and torpedoes.

What an Oscillator Does

Now you probably want to know what an oscillator does that makes it so important.

An oscillator does nothing more than put out an AC voltage at a desired frequency. The audio signal generator used in working with audio amplifiers is an audio oscillator. The audio oscillator shown below puts out an AC voltage at any frequency from 0 to 15,000 cycles per second. The RF signal generator used in working with RF amplifiers is an RF oscillator, and the RF oscillator shown below can put out an AC voltage at any frequency from 215,000 cycles to 22,000,000 cycles. Both these oscillators. supply a test signal that enable you to check and troubleshoot amplifiers.

A radio transmitter takes a high frequency AC voltage, amplifies it, and then radiates this amplified signal to distant points by means of a transmitter antenna. Where does this high frequency AC voltage come from? ...From an oscillator. A radio transmitter is nothing more than an oscillator with some high power RF amplifiers to step up the oscillator signal so that it can be radiated long distances by the antenna. (See Volume 4.)

The most advanced type of radio receiver, the superheterodyne receiver, also contains oscillator circuits. (See Volume 5.)

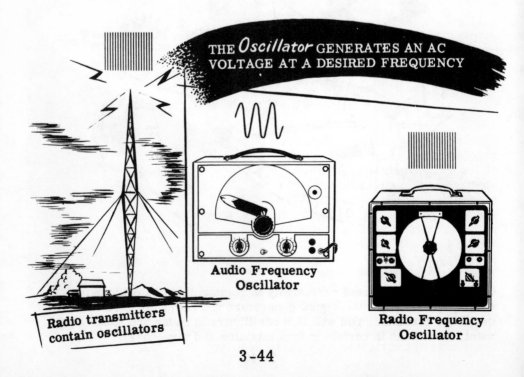

THE *Oscillator* GENERATES AN AC VOLTAGE AT A DESIRED FREQUENCY

Audio Frequency
Oscillator

Radio transmitters
contain oscillators

Radio Frequency
Oscillator

What Oscillations Are

If anything swings back and forth in a uniform way it is said to be "oscillating." A violin string "oscillates" when a bow is drawn over it. A swing moving back and forth "oscillates." A pendulum swinging on a clock "oscillates."

Some Common Oscillators

A VIOLIN STRING OSCILLATES

A CHILD'S SWING

Consider the pendulum. When it reaches the extreme left-hand side of its swing, it comes to rest momentarily, and all its energy is stored as "potential energy." Half way through its swing, it is moving at its greatest speed, and all its energy has been converted to "kinetic energy," or "energy of motion." When it completes one swing, arriving at the extreme right-hand position, it again comes momentarily to rest, and its energy is all "potential" once again. We can represent this motion by one-half a sine wave, plotting velocity against time. Velocity toward the right is considered positive.

This motion can be represented by this

What Oscillations Are (continued)

Since the return swing from right to left is a reversal of direction, the second half of the sine curve is shown below the line. Thus one complete cycle of oscillation of the pendulum may be represented by one complete cycle of the sine wave.

..ONE COMPLETE
CYCLE OF OSCILLATION

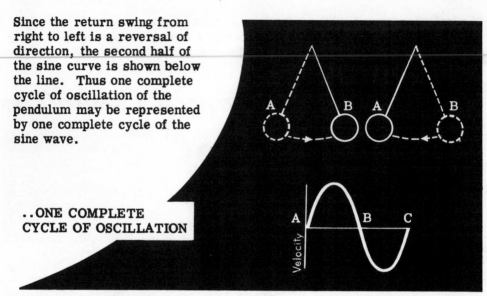

Did you ever notice that one complete trip on the swing takes the same time as any other trip? You can represent three cycles of the swing like this: the time from t_1 to t_3 is the same as that from t_3 to t_5 or that from t_5 to t_7, as shown below. Also the time required for the various half cycles (t_1 to t_2, t_2 to t_3, etc.) is always the same.

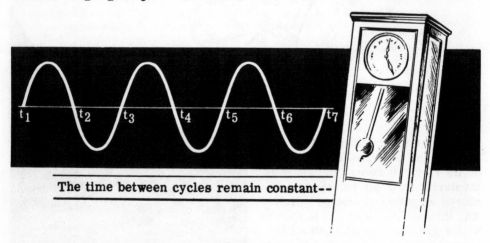

The time between cycles remain constant--

Clocks and watches keep accurate time because the time consumed by any one swing of the pendulum or balance wheel is the same as that for any other swing. This is as true of the seventh swing as it is of the first. Now you understand what was meant by the statement that an oscillator moves back and forth in a uniform way. Two conditions exist when something oscillates: (1) there must be back and forth motion (vibration) and (2) the period of time for each back and forth motion must be the same (uniform).

What Oscillations Are (continued)

You know that the motion of a swing will eventually run down. You know, too, that this loss of energy is due to friction, and to compensate for this loss additional outside energy must be supplied in a uniform way. What happens when outside energy is not supplied can be shown by this curve:

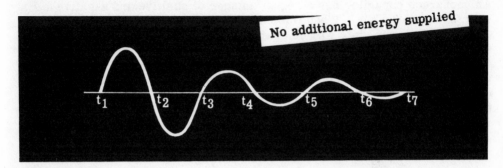

No additional energy supplied

This is called a "damped" wave. It is like a sine wave, but with the height (amplitude) of successive cycles diminishing gradually. The time interval remains the same.

How would you supply the necessary energy to prevent "damping?" If you were pushing a child on a swing you would not make the next push until the swing had just completed its arc, and was about to reverse its direction. This application of energy at the proper point or with the proper timing, is "in phase" with the original motion. To supply energy to an oscillator in order to support its natural period of oscillations, the outside source of energy must be in phase with the natural period of the oscillator.

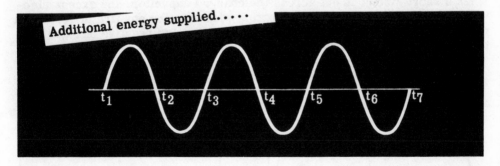

Additional energy supplied.....

You know now that to support a stable oscillator, two conditions are necessary:

1. Energy must be supplied to compensate for loss of energy in the oscillator.

2. When supplied, the outside source of energy must be in phase with the natural period of the oscillator.

The Electronic Oscillator

An electronic oscillator is a simple circuit—it consists of a capacitor
and a coil connected in parallel. To understand how such a circuit can be
made to oscillate, suppose you consider what happens when a capacitor is
charged and discharged.

An uncharged capacitor has an equal number of positive and negative
charges on each plate. When this capacitor is connected across a source
of DC voltage, one plate will be charged negatively and the other will be
charged positively. What has happened is that there are more than the
original number of electrons on the negative plate, and less than the original number of electrons on the positive plate. In addition, the excess of
electrons on the negative plate is exactly equal to the loss of electrons on
the positive plate.

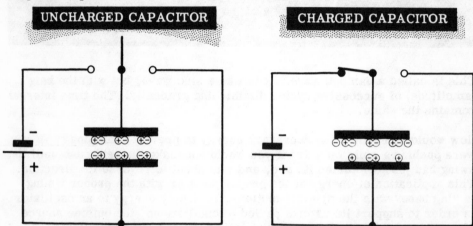

When a short circuit is put across the charged capacitor, the excess electrons are attracted through the shorting wire onto the positive plate. Each
plate once more has an equal number of positive and negative charges and
the capacitor is uncharged.

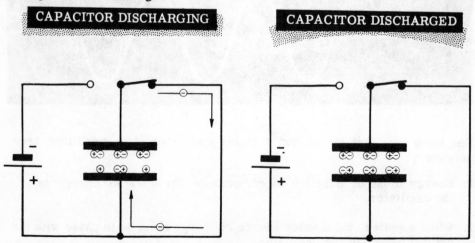

The Electronic Oscillator (continued)

On the previous sheet you saw what would happen if a short circuit were connected across the charged capacitor. If an inductance is connected across the charged capacitor, the results are quite different.

You will remember from your work in Basic Electricity that an inductance has a peculiar electrical characteristic—it resists any change of electron current through itself. You remember that when current flows through a coil, a magnetic field is generated around the coil. Any change in the current causes the magnetic field to expand or contract. This expansion or contraction of the magnetic field causes the magnetic lines to cut across the turns of the coil—resulting in the generation of a voltage which opposes the change in current.

When the charged capacitor is switched across the coil, (1) in the illustration below, the electrons stored on the negative plate cannot rush through the coil onto the positive plate and the voltage across the circuit is a maximum. As soon as a small number of electrons flow into the coil, a magnetic field starts to build up. This building up of the magnetic field induces a voltage across the coil which opposes the flow of electrons from the negative plate. The capacitor and coil act like two dry cells connected in series, opposing—positive to positive and negative to negative. As a result, the charged capacitor cannot discharge immediately through the coil. The larger the coil, the longer it takes for the capacitor to discharge. As the capacitor discharges, the magnetic field about the coil becomes stronger and stronger, and the voltage continues to decrease (2).

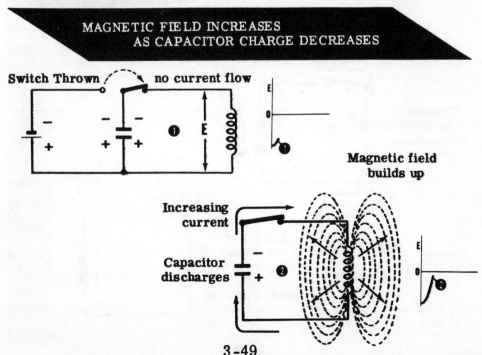

MAGNETIC FIELD INCREASES
AS CAPACITOR CHARGE DECREASES

Switch Thrown — no current flow

Magnetic field builds up

Increasing current

Capacitor discharges

The Electronic Oscillator (continued)

By the time the capacitor has completely discharged, all of its electrical energy has been transformed into magnetic field energy around the coil. As soon as the current through the coil begins to decrease, the magnetic field begins to collapse around the coil (3). The collapsing magnetic lines cut across the turns of the coil and induce a voltage across the coil. This induced voltage prevents the current through the coil from decreasing, and it is opposite in polarity to the original voltage across the capacitor. Now the capacitor and coil act like two dry cells connected in series, aiding— negative to positive. Because of this induced voltage, electrons are forced to flow through the coil in the same direction. Electrons are stripped off the upper plate of the capacitor and forced through the coil onto the lower plate.

All of the energy of the collapsing magnetic field goes into forcing a negative charge on the lower capacitor plate. By the time the field has completely collapsed, all of the magnetic energy has been returned to the capacitor as an electric charge, and the voltage across the capacitor is exactly opposite in polarity to the original charge (4).

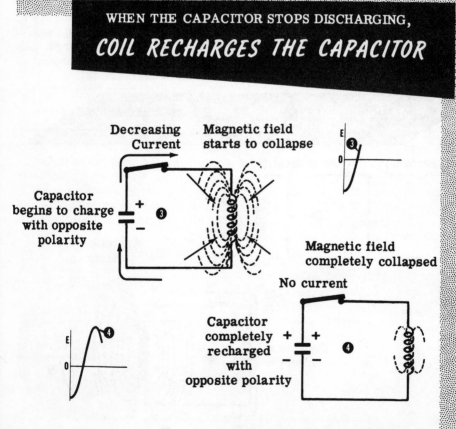

WHEN THE CAPACITOR STOPS DISCHARGING,

COIL RECHARGES THE CAPACITOR

Decreasing Current

Magnetic field starts to collapse

Capacitor begins to charge with opposite polarity

Magnetic field completely collapsed

No current

Capacitor completely recharged with opposite polarity

The Electronic Oscillator (continued)

Now that the electrons are all stored on the lower plate of the capacitor, the charge is exactly the opposite to what it was originally. The electrons are now attracted to the upper positive plate through the coil. As the capacitor discharges, a magnetic field builds up around the coil (5). The collapse of this magnetic field forces additional electrons off the lower plate onto the upper plate. By the time the magnetic field has completely collapsed (6), all the electrons are back on the upper plate, and the situation is exactly the same as when the capacitor was first charged. The entire cycle then repeats itself over and over again. Electrical energy is alternately stored as a charge on a capacitor and a magnetic field around a coil. This is what is meant by electronic oscillation.

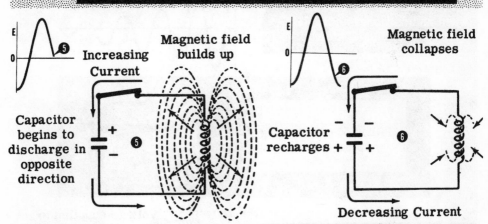

RECHARGING CAPACITOR TO ORIGINAL CONDITION

If an oscilloscope were connected in parallel across the coil and capacitor, the rise and fall of voltage would appear as a sine wave if there were no resistance in any part of the circuit. If there were no resistance in the circuit, the oscillations would continue indefinitely. However, resistance cannot be eliminated completely from any circuit, and some of the electrical energy of oscillation is dissipated by the resistance as heat. Due to this loss of electrical energy, the voltage becomes lower and lower on each swing and the oscillation eventually disappears.

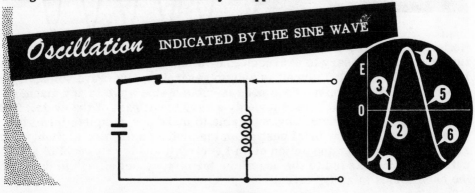

Oscillation INDICATED BY THE SINE WAVE

The Electronic Oscillator (continued)

In order to make the oscillations continue indefinitely, enough electrical energy must be put back into the LC circuit (called the "tank circuit") to overcome the losses due to resistance. In addition, this electrical energy must be put back into the circuit at just the right moment so that it will give a little extra "push" or "kick" at the proper time. This electrical kick corresponds to the push given to a swing at the end of its arc.

One way of supplying this electrical push to the LC circuit is to switch a source of voltage across the capacitor just at the moment when the capacitor is reaching its full charge. In this manner, oscillations can be made to continue indefinitely.

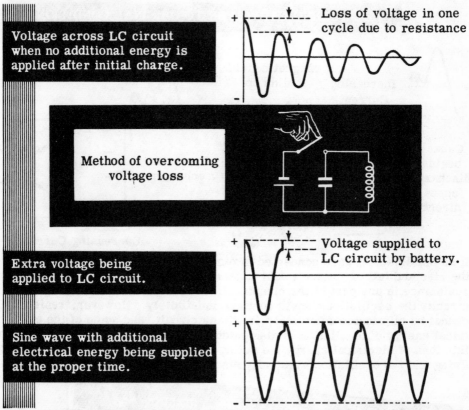

Voltage across LC circuit when no additional energy is applied after initial charge.

Loss of voltage in one cycle due to resistance

Method of overcoming voltage loss

Voltage supplied to LC circuit by battery.

Extra voltage being applied to LC circuit.

Sine wave with additional electrical energy being supplied at the proper time.

Notice that the only kick the oscillator circuit receives is the small fraction of a volt necessary to overcome the voltage drop due to the resistance in the circuit. The LC circuit is able to generate a sine wave voltage even though the kick it receives does not resemble a sine wave in any manner and even though the kick lasts for only a very small part of the cycle. The flywheel on a one-cylinder engine is able to make one complete turn when it receives only a very brief push from the piston on each revolution. This resemblance between the action of an LC circuit and the flywheel of a one-cylinder engine has led to the use of the term "flywheel effect" to describe the oscillations in an LC circuit.

The Feedback Circuit

The method of supplying extra energy to the LC circuit described on the previous sheet would work very well if there were some switching arrangement that could work at the frequencies required. Some oscillators must be able to work at frequencies well over 100 million cycles per second, and it is quite obvious that no mechanical switch could work at this speed. The answer to supplying electrical energy at the proper instant is to use a vacuum tube circuit.

By connecting the LC circuit to the grid of a vacuum tube, the oscillating voltage can be amplified. If a small portion of this amplified voltage can be fed back in the proper phase, enough electrical energy will be put back into the LC circuit to overcome the resistance losses in the LC circuit. The vacuum tube used in an oscillator does not do any oscillating—it is the LC circuit that oscillates, and it is the vacuum tube that gives the kick.

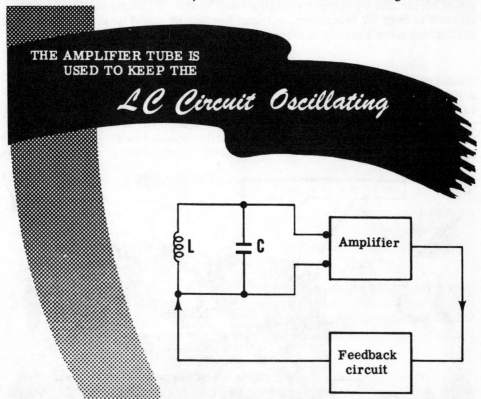

THE AMPLIFIER TUBE IS
USED TO KEEP THE

LC Circuit Oscillating

All the oscillators you will learn about in this section operate on the principle illustrated above. The major difference between various oscillators is the method in which a voltage is fed back to the LC circuit in proper phase. You will learn about six basic oscillators: the Armstrong, the Colpitts, the Hartley, the tuned-plate—tuned-grid, the crystal controlled and the electron-coupled oscillators. You will see how these oscillators work, and the advantages and disadvantages of each type.

Frequency Stability of Oscillators

One important characteristic of oscillators, which you are going to learn about, is frequency stability. Although you have not yet studied oscillators, it ought to be obvious that an oscillator should maintain the frequency to which it is set. Unfortunately, all oscillators tend to drift in frequency unless steps are taken to prevent this. Some circuits drift less than others.

Imagine what would happen if frequency drift were not taken into account. If one ship were trying to contact another, and the oscillator in its transmitter drifted off frequency, the message would never be received. If the oscillator in a shipboard receiver drifted off frequency, that ship would receive no messages at all. If the oscillator in a shipboard sonar unit drifted off frequency, that ship could not detect submarines. It would be torpedoed by the first enemy submarine that came along. A great proportion of electronic equipment contains oscillators. If these oscillators were allowed to drift off frequency, all this equipment would be useless until the oscillators were reset to the correct frequency.

Thus you can see that it is necessary to understand frequency stability and drift. Drift is caused by several factors. Vibration, varying loads and varying supply voltages will cause an oscillator to drift. Changes in temperature will, also. Since much electronic equipment is subject to all of these factors, some compensation is usually included in all equipment which contains an oscillator. You will learn about these things in the next few topics.

FACTORS WHICH CAUSE FREQUENCY SHIFTS IN OSCILLATORS.

The Armstrong Oscillator

Basically all oscillators operate in the same way. Energy is coupled back, from the output to the tuned oscillating circuit on the input of the vacuum tube, in order to compensate for inevitable heat losses due to electrical resistance. If the losses are compensated for, oscillations continue. If you understand how oscillations are maintained in the Armstrong oscillator, you will understand the basic principles underlying all oscillators.

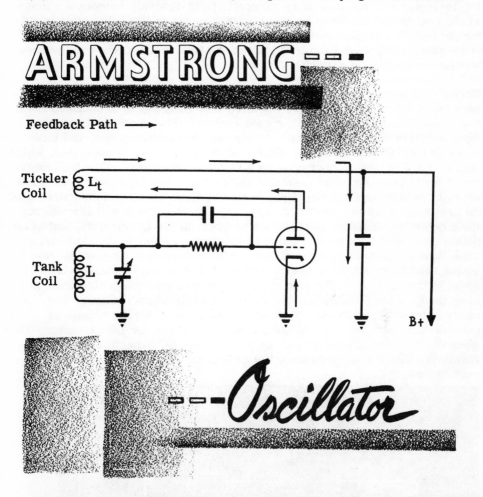

The Armstrong oscillator is like an RF amplifier with one modification: a coil has been introduced into the plate circuit. This coil is called the "tickler coil." It is wound adjacent to the LC tank coil (usually both coils are wound on the same coil form), so when plate current flows through this tickler coil, L_t, an emf will be induced into the tank coil L. Actually it is not DC plate current but variations in this DC current which produce the changing magnetic fields responsible for induced voltages across the tank coil. The induced voltage is the feedback voltage which sustains oscillation.

The Armstrong Oscillator (continued)

Grid Leak Bias

There is nothing complicated about the operation of the Armstrong oscillator. When the power supply is turned on, a flow of electrons surges from the cathode to the plate and through the tickler coil to B+. This surge of current causes a rapid buildup of a magnetic field around the tickler coil, and this expanding magnetic field suddenly induces a voltage in the coil of the LC circuit. This voltage surge in the LC circuit is sufficient to begin oscillations. All that the tube and tickler coil have to do from now on is give a voltage "kick" to the LC circuit at the proper time during the cycle of oscillation.

Notice that no cathode resistor or battery bias is used in the Armstrong oscillator circuit. The proper negative bias on the grid is obtained from the resistor and capacitor in the grid circuit. This method of obtaining bias is called "grid leak" bias. As you will very shortly see, the tube must be biased well below cut-off for most of its cycle of operation, which means that the tube is operating as a Class C amplifier. This high negative bias is maintained by means of the grid and the capacitor in the grid circuit. When plate current first begins to flow, there is no negative bias on the grid. This means that a very large plate current will flow through the tickler coil (causing oscillations to begin in the LC circuit), and in addition there will be a sudden pulse of electron current in the grid circuit. This flow of electrons causes a voltage to be developed across the resistor, and this voltage is such that the grid is strongly negative with respect to the cathode. The grid capacitor stores up enough electrons to keep the grid negative for nearly all of the cycle of oscillation. The charge on the negative side of the grid capacitor is strong enough to counterbalance a positive charge on the top plate of the LC capacitor. Only when the positive charge on the top plate of the LC capacitor reaches its maximum will it counterbalance the grid capacitor and cause plate current to flow.

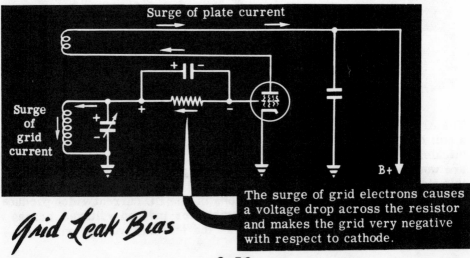

Surge of plate current

Surge of grid current

B+

The surge of grid electrons causes a voltage drop across the resistor and makes the grid very negative with respect to cathode.

Grid Leak Bias

The Armstrong Oscillator (continued)

How Oscillations Are Maintained

Now that a cycle of oscillation has begun and the grid is negative with respect to the cathode, suppose you analyze what happens through an entire cycle of oscillation.

Begin your analysis at a time when the electrons are arriving on the top plate of the tuning capacitor after travelling through the coil from the bottom plate. At this time the negative charge on the grid capacitor is strong enough to counterbalance the decreasing positive charge on the top of the LC capacitor, and no plate current flows.

After the upper plate of the capacitor has reached its maximum negative charge, the electrons begin to flow back through the coil to the bottom plate. As the electrons begin to accumulate on the bottom plate, the top plate becomes more and more positive with respect to the bottom plate. The only thing that prevents the grid from becoming positive is the fact that all of the electrons on the charged capacitor have not leaked off through the grid resistor and the grid capacitor can still counteract the positive voltage at the top of the LC circuit. No plate current has flowed up to this time.

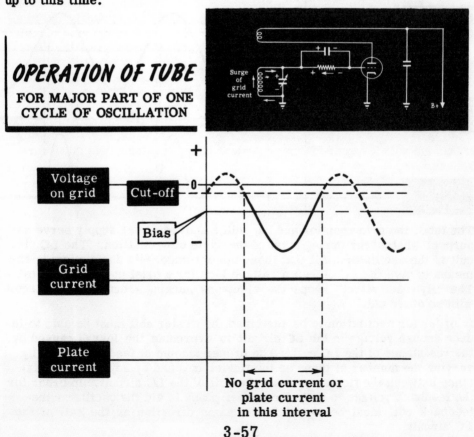

OPERATION OF TUBE
FOR MAJOR PART OF ONE
CYCLE OF OSCILLATION

Surge
of
grid
current

B+

Voltage
on grid

Cut-off

0

Bias

+

−

Grid
current

Plate
current

No grid current or
plate current
in this interval

The Armstrong Oscillator (continued)

How Oscillations Are Maintained

Finally the top of the LC circuit becomes so positive that it briefly over-comes the negative bias maintained by the grid capacitor. At this time plate current begins to flow and continues to flow for the interval that the top of the LC circuit remains strongly positive. This brief surge of plate current flows through the tickler coil and induces a brief voltage surge in the LC circuit. The tickler coil is wound in the same direction as the coil in the LC circuit, so this voltage surge is in such a direction as to give a "push" to aid the flow of electrons in the LC circuit. During the short interval that the top of the LC circuit is strongly positive, grid cur-rent begins to flow and causes the grid capacitor to regain its strong negative charge.

Immediately after the top plate of the LC capacitor reaches its peak posi-tive value, electrons begin leaving the bottom plate of the capacitor on their way to the top plate. The negative charge on the grid capacitor is now strong enough to cut off all plate current and you are back at the point where you began your analysis. This cycle repeats itself over and over again.

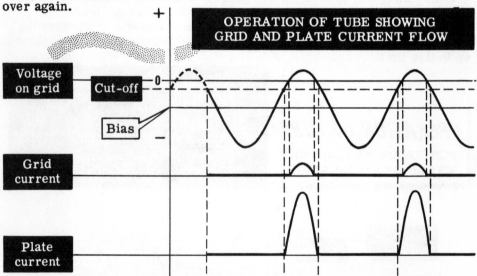

The tube, the grid resistor and capacitor and the power supply serve no purpose whatsoever during most of the cycle of oscillation. The LC cir-cuit is the oscillator. All that these other components do is provide the means to give the LC circuit a voltage kick for a brief portion of the cycle. The "flywheel effect" keeps the electrons surging around the LC circuit with no other aid.

In order for oscillation to be sustained, the tickler coil must be able to in-duce enough voltage in the LC circuit to overcome the losses caused by the resistance of the LC coil. The proper amount of feedback is set by varying the number of turns on the tickler coil and by adjusting the dis-tance between the tickler coil and the coil of the LC circuit. In order for the feedback voltage to be in the proper phase to aid the oscillator, the feedback coil must be wound in the same direction as the coil of the LC circuit.

The Frequency of Oscillation

The most important thing to remember about oscillators is that the tank circuit does the oscillating; the tube merely supplies the pulses to keep the oscillations in the tank from dying down. Therefore, it should be obvious that the tank circuit determines the frequency of oscillation. Here is how this occurs.

You know that in any vacuum tube, the voltage on the grid controls the amount of plate current. If the voltage on the grid varies 1000 times per second, the plate current will have that many variations. If the plate current varies 1000 times per second, then the feedback pulses will be timed at the same rate. Now the question is: what started the oscillator off at this frequency in the first place?

The answer to that question is—the tank coil. When a pulse of current is delivered to a parallel-resonant circuit, the resonant circuit will start oscillating at its own resonant frequency. It doesn't matter what waveshape the pulse has; the tank will oscillate sinusoidally and at its natural resonant frequency, which depends on the value of L and C in the tank circuit. The larger L and C are, the lower the frequency. As L and C decrease, the frequency increases. Since it is more convenient to vary C than L, a variable capacitor is placed in the tank circuit to control the frequency of oscillation.

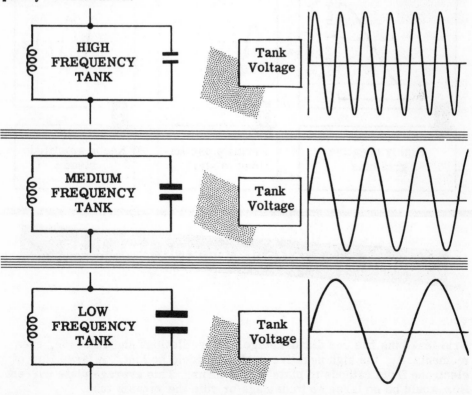

Advantages of Grid Leak Bias

An important feature of the grid leak bias method used in the Armstrong oscillator is that it tends to make the oscillator self-adjusting. A random change in plate voltage affects the amplitude of oscillation, but high grid bias tends to reduce or cushion this effect. Here is how this cushioning effect acts:

1. If plate voltage rises, plate current increases through the tickler coil.
2. A larger emf is induced in the LC circuit.
3. The negative charge on the grid capacitor increases.
4. Plate current is reduced to its original level.

This grid bias tends to cancel plate current changes and reduce its effect on the LC tank.

Summing up the effects of grid leak bias: it permits high grid bias, permits oscillations to start, and tends to keep the strength of oscillation steady.

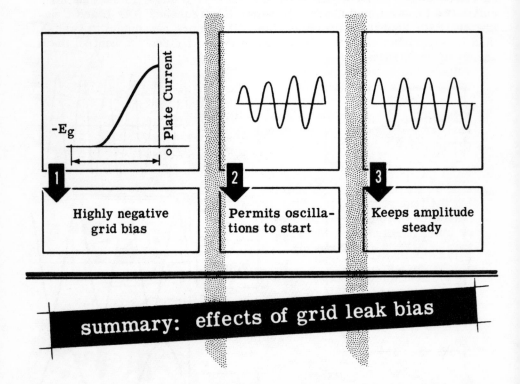

Highly negative grid bias	Permits oscilla-tions to start

Keeps amplitude steady

summary: effects of grid leak bias

Grid leak bias has one disadvantage. If oscillations should cease, even momentarily, the high negative grid bias would be lost. A large flow of electrons from cathode to plate would occur. This average plate current flow would be so large as to damage or ruin the vacuum tube.

Frequency Instability

In your study of the Armstrong oscillator you have found out about a typical feedback circuit, an LC tank oscillator, and grid bias. Actually the Armstrong oscillator is rarely used, for it has several shortcomings, the most serious of which is frequency instability.

The tank consists of a coil and capacitor, and these determine its frequency of oscillation. However, this frequency of oscillation is subject to change due to other factors. Here are some of the factors which may cause a shift in frequency, and ways of eliminating them:

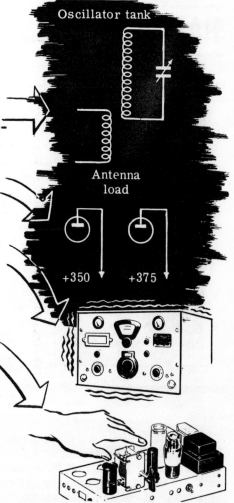

1. <u>Drawing Power from the Tank:</u> Load changes which draw power from the tank circuit, causing the tank voltage to drop, can be reduced by using an amplifier to separate the load from the oscillator.

2. <u>Changes in Plate Voltage:</u> Plate voltage can be kept constant by using voltage regulators.

3. <u>Vibration and Shock:</u> Shock absorbers and bonding on the circuit components reduce vibration.

4. <u>Hand Capacitance:</u> Grounding one side of the tank circuit or shielding the tank reduces the added capacitance introduced by the hands or other parts of the body when they pass by the tank circuit.

5. <u>Heat:</u> Heat effects can be eliminated by placing circuit components in thermostatically regulated compartments.

The importance of maintaining a stable frequency becomes apparent when you realize that most transmitting stations operate at one fixed frequency. At times it is essential that transmitter and receiver maintain constant twenty-four hour communications relations. If the frequency shifted, vital messages or parts of them might never be received.

The Hartley Oscillator

You are now going to learn about the Hartley oscillator. You will find that it represents an improvement over the Armstrong oscillator in the method of coupling. While it suffers from frequency instability, it has many favorable features, being adaptable to a wide range of frequencies and easy to tune. Since the Hartley oscillator is a widely used circuit, you should make sure that you understand it thoroughly.

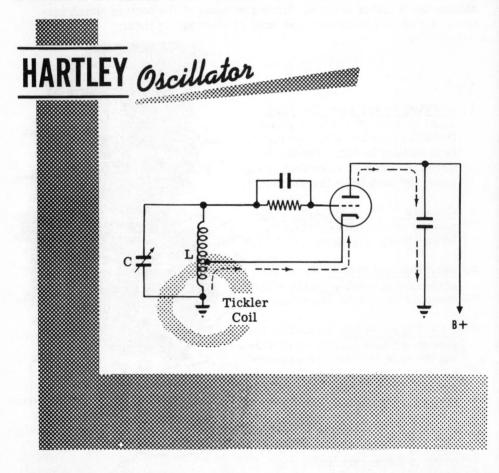

There is very little difference between the Armstrong and Hartley oscillators. In the Armstrong type, oscillations are sustained by a voltage kick induced in the LC circuit by a pulse of plate current through the tickler coil. In the Hartley type, the voltage kick is also induced in the LC circuit by a pulse of cathode current through the tickler coil. The unusual thing about the Hartley circuit is that the tickler coil is part of the coil which makes up the LC circuit. This single coil is tapped in such a way that the cathode current flows through the lower part of the coil and induces a kick voltage in the grid portion of the coil. The amount of feedback voltage induced can be adjusted by moving the cathode tap.

How Oscillation Is Maintained in the Hartley Oscillator

Oscillations start when the B+ supply is turned on, because of the sudden rise in plate current. The DC current path is: flow of electrons from cathode to plate to B+, through the power supply to ground, up through L1 and so back to cathode. There is no grid bias, initially, to block the flow of plate current. This initial surge of current through L1 induces a voltage kick in L2 and oscillations begin. In the meantime, a pulse of grid current has charged the grid capacitor highly negative in exactly the same manner as in the Armstrong oscillator.

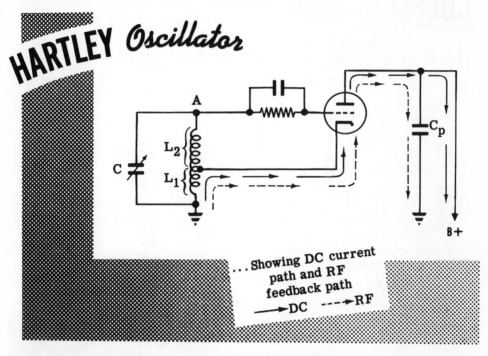

HARTLEY *Oscillator*

... Showing DC current path and RF feedback path
——→ DC   ----→ RF

Once oscillation has begun, the cycle is very much the same as in the Armstrong oscillator. The tube is biased below cut-off from shortly after the top plate of the LC circuit, point A, has reached its peak positive value until shortly before it reaches its peak positive value again. During all this time the tube serves no purpose whatsoever, and the surge of electrons through the tank circuit goes on solely because of the flywheel effect of that LC circuit.

When the electrons in the tank circuit begin to pile up on the lower plate of the capacitor, the upper plate becomes more and more positive. For the brief interval that the top plate of the LC circuit is at its peak positive voltage, this positive voltage is able to counteract the negative bias caused by the grid capacitor. During the brief instant that the grid remains positive, a pulse of cathode current flows and induces a voltage kick in L2. The flow of grid current recharges the grid capacitor highly negative and the cycle begins over again.

The Colpitts Oscillator

The third basic oscillator you will learn about is the Colpitts oscillator.
It is versatile, easy to operate, adaptable to a wide range of frequencies and
has somewhat better frequency stability than the Hartley oscillator. It is very
much like the Hartley, but uses tapped capacitance in place of the Hartley's
tapped inductance for feedback. The two are compared below.

COLPITTS *Oscillator*

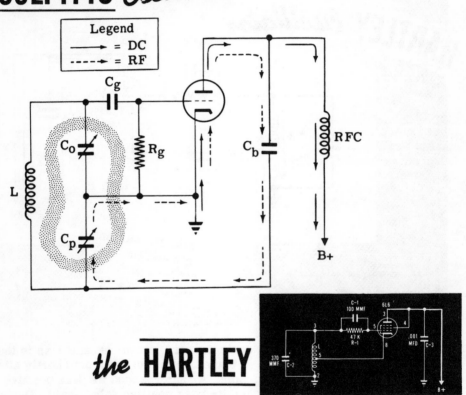

Legend
→ = DC
----→ = RF

the **HARTLEY**

The DC current path is: electron flow from cathode to plate, through the
RF choke to B+, through the power supply to ground, back to cathode.

AC current is coupled back to the tank by means of the coupling capacitor
Cb; and Cp is the AC plate load across which the feedback voltage is developed. Feedback current begins due to the first rise in plate current.
The amount of feedback depends on the ratio of Cp to Co. Proper phasing
of oscillation is obtained with the grid and plate at opposite ends of the
tank, using a condenser, Cb, for feedback of RF voltage. The current
oscillates in the tank circuit consisting of LCpCo, and the reactance of the
coil and two capacitors determine the oscillating frequency.

Review

All vacuum tube oscillators, whether RF or audio, work on the principle of feeding back voltage pulses from the plate circuit to the grid circuit of the tube. The grid is connected to a parallel resonant circuit which does the oscillating. The parallel resonant circuit also times the pulses fed back, and thus controls the frequency of oscillation. The tube is generally operated Class C, so that plate current flows in pulses (during less than half of the AC cycle).

THE ARMSTRONG OSCILLATOR— uses a tickler coil to feed back pulses from the plate circuit to the tank circuit.

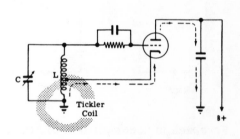

HARTLEY OSCILLATOR—uses a tapped coil instead of a separate tickler winding to feed back pulses. It has more frequency stability than the Armstrong.

COLPITTS OSCILLATOR—uses a tapped capacitance network to couple the feedback pulses to the grid tank circuit. It has more frequency stability than the Hartley oscillator.

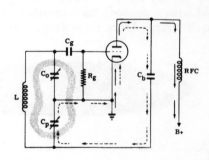

GRID LEAK BIAS—a method of bias in which excess electrons accumulate on the grid, producing a negative bias. They are allowed to leak off slowly through a large resistor which is placed in parallel with the grid capacitor or from grid to cathode. Making the resistor large enough produces more than cut-off bias and results in Class C operation.

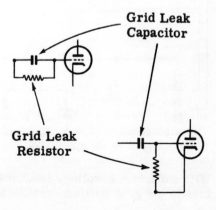

Grid Leak Capacitor

Grid Leak Resistor

Introduction

The tuned-plate tuned-grid oscillator (TPTG) is an oscillator which is not widely used as such, but one whose principles are employed in the crystal oscillator which you will learn about a little later.

The distinctive feature of the TPTG is the fact that the output as well as the input circuit is tuned. Also distinctive is the fact that no coupling capacitor or coil is necessary if a triode is used.

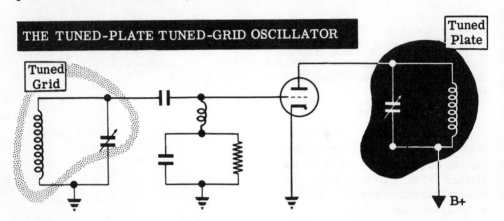

THE TUNED-PLATE TUNED-GRID OSCILLATOR

Tuned Grid

Tuned Plate

B+

Feedback is accomplished without using either capacitor or coil to couple the energy back. To prove this, suppose you start with the above circuit, but with a pentode tube in place of a triode and use link coupling to feed back energy from plate to grid tuned circuit.

A PENTODE WITH LINK COUPLING *For Feedback*

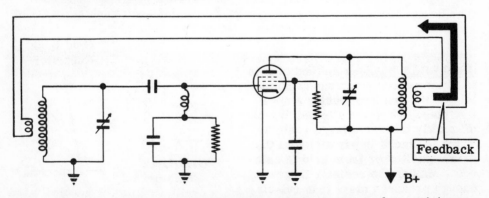

Feedback

B+

With sufficient coupling, feedback energy will compensate for resistance loss in the grid tank and oscillation will continue.

Feedback in the TPTG Oscillator

Replace the link coil with a small capacitor, say of 3 mmf capacity. This capacitor will provide the feedback.

Now you are ready to compare this circuit, containing a pentode with capacitor feedback, to a circuit containing a triode but without capacitor feedback.

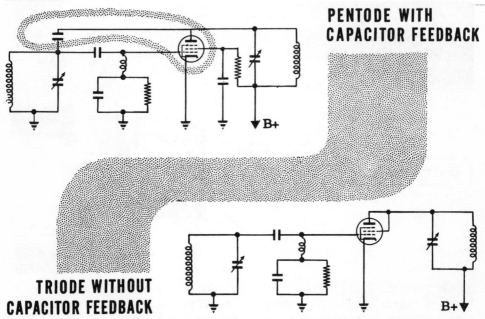

PENTODE WITH CAPACITOR FEEDBACK

TRIODE WITHOUT CAPACITOR FEEDBACK

The pentode with capacitor feedback will support oscillation. The triode without capacitor feedback will support oscillation because it, too, provides feedback: not through an outside capacitor but through the capacitance between the plate and the grid of the triode. The pentode has such a low plate-grid electrode capacitance that an added capacitor is needed. The triode has more plate-grid capacitance and doesn't require an added capacitor. Both employ capacitance feedback.

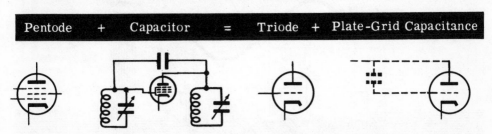

Pentode + Capacitor = Triode + Plate-Grid Capacitance

Thus you can see that feedback to sustain oscillation can be accomplished without the use of coil or capacitor. The internal capacitance of tube elements provides the feedback.

Introduction to Crystal Oscillators

The crystal-controlled oscillator, or simply the crystal oscillator, is very widely used because it has one quality which none of the previously studied oscillators has—high frequency stability. Crystals have very many uses apart from their use in oscillators, being found in many receivers, microphones and loudspeakers. The crystals most commonly used in radio transmitters are quartz, tourmaline and Rochelle Salts.

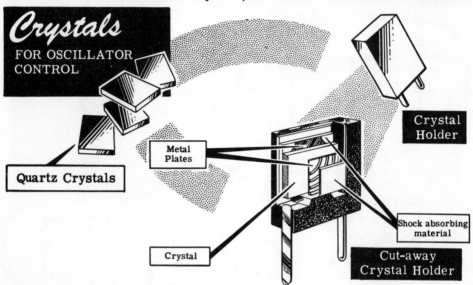

These crystals exhibit what is known as the piezoelectric effect. If a block of quartz is placed between two metal plates and pressure is applied, then a voltage difference will appear across those two plates. Also, if an AC voltage is applied across the two plates, the crystal will stretch and compress. Thus the crystal can convert mechanical pressure into electrical energy and electrical energy into mechanical vibration.

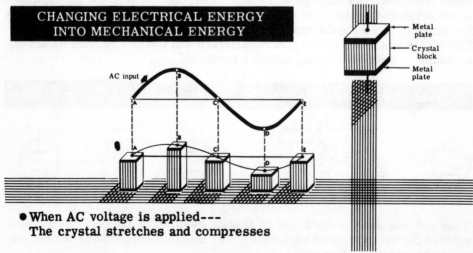

- When AC voltage is applied---
  The crystal stretches and compresses

The Crystal as a Resonator

A crystal has a natural frequency of vibration. When the AC voltage across its faces has the same frequency as the mechanical frequency of the crystal, the crystal block will stretch and compress more than for other frequencies. Also, the crystal's natural frequency of vibration is extraordinarily constant, more constant even than the frequency of oscillation in an LC circuit.

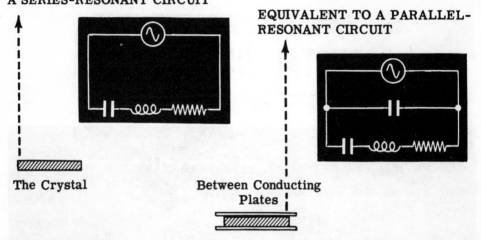

EQUIVALENT TO A SERIES-RESONANT CIRCUIT

The Crystal

EQUIVALENT TO A PARALLEL-RESONANT CIRCUIT

Between Conducting Plates

Taken by itself, the crystal acts like a series-resonant circuit. Together with its two plates, it acts like a parallel-resonant circuit. The frequency at which it vibrates depends on its thickness. Thick crystals vibrate slowly, thin crystals vibrate rapidly.

For protection from mechanical shock, crystals have been placed in sealed containers or holders. Don't drop them. Crystals should be protected from electrical shock, too. Excessive voltage causes them to crack or overheat. The RF current flowing through the crystal should not exceed 100 milliamperes.

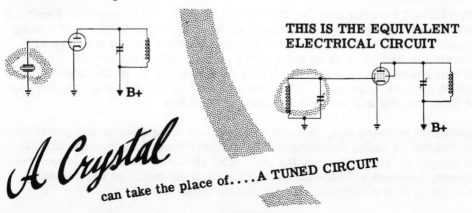

THIS IS THE EQUIVALENT ELECTRICAL CIRCUIT

A Crystal can take the place of....A TUNED CIRCUIT

The Crystal Oscillator Circuit

Where power output is not the most important consideration and where only one fixed frequency is to be used, the crystal oscillator is a highly satisfactory circuit. It overcomes one defect which all previous oscillators have suffered from, namely, its frequency is not influenced by changes of load.

The basic crystal oscillator uses a crystal as a mechanical resonator, in place of the tuned-grid capacitor and inductor in a TPTG oscillator.

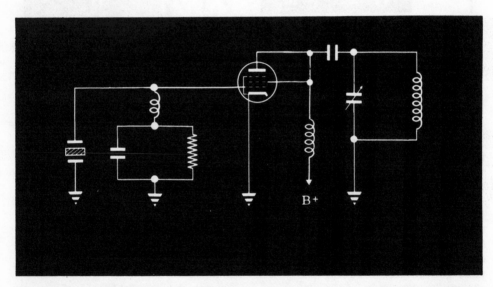

This circuit behaves like the TPTG oscillator in every respect. Feedback is obtained through the plate-grid capacity of the vacuum tube or by using a small feedback capacitor. This voltage feedback causes the crystal to vibrate mechanically at its natural frequency. When the crystal vibrates, an emf appears across the electrodes on the two faces of the crystal. This emf is applied to the grid. The changing emf on the grid controls the flow of plate current and hence the amount of feedback.

Amount of coupling and, therefore, amplitude of oscillation and power output depend on tuning the plate tank to a higher frequency than the natural frequency of the crystal. If the plate tank should be tuned to a lower frequency, feedback through the plate-grid capacity would be out-of-phase with the grid oscillations, and oscillation would cease.

Tuning the Crystal Oscillator

To tune the crystal oscillator you tune the plate tank capacitor, starting with the capacitor set for maximum capacity. A plate current meter indicates a high plate current, as is to be expected when the grid tank is not oscillating. This plate current suddenly drops to point A, indicating that the plate is at the same resonant frequency as the crystal circuit, hence feedback is at a maximum and oscillations are very strong. The capacitor is tuned past this point to the region B-C, where plate current has risen and the plate tank is higher in frequency than the grid crystal oscillator. Some power is sacrificed for stable oscillations, since at point A any small change in the direction of lowered frequency would cause the crystal to stop vibrating.

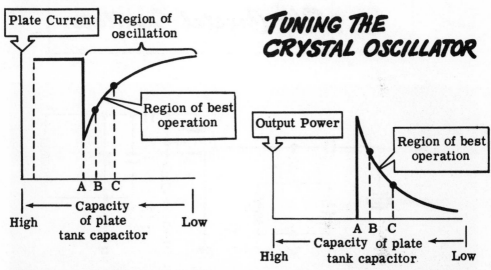

TUNING THE CRYSTAL OSCILLATOR

Since a crystal has low frictional losses, it doesn't require much feedback to sustain oscillations. Besides, a large amount of voltage across the crystal plates can make the crystal vibrate so hard as to overheat or shatter—much as a powerful explosion causes window panes to vibrate so strongly as to shatter. Overheating causes frequency drift. Thus, smaller feedback results in a greater safety factor and in less frequency drift.

Since a pentode tube has very low grid-plate capacity, it may be used in a high frequency crystal oscillator to lessen the amount of feedback. This allows the crystal to do less work while still controlling the frequency of oscillation. Such a circuit has still less frequency drift than a triode crystal oscillator and is often used when very precise frequency measurements are being made.

However, the pentode crystal oscillator suffers from certain disadvantages. At low frequencies, the low grid-plate capacity of the pentode does not allow enough feedback to sustain oscillations. Therefore, some external grid-plate capacity must be inserted. The crystal oscillator you will build avoids this difficulty by connecting the oscillator tube as a triode.

Analysis of the Crystal Oscillator

The crystal oscillator is a TPTG oscillator in which a crystal substitutes for the conventional tuned capacitor and inductor. The 6L6 tube (see figure) is used as a triode. Thus the grid-plate capacity is much higher than if the tube were connected as a pentode. This increases the amount of feedback and makes the crystal "work harder." It is possible to use a pentode in a crystal oscillator, but such an oscillator is more complicated and sometimes more difficult to adjust. To avoid the possibility of this difficulty, the 6L6 is connected as a triode.

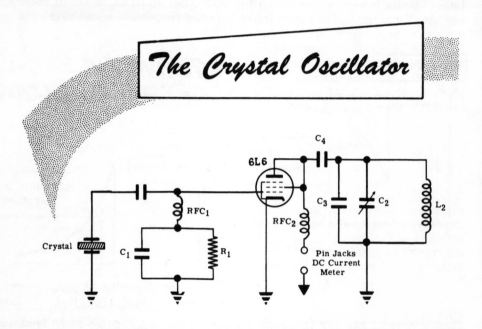

The Crystal Oscillator

C_3 in parallel with C_2 adds to its capacity and reduces the resonant frequency. This is required if the range of C_2L_2 alone does not extend down to the crystal frequency.

RFC_2 is the plate choke which keeps the RF out of the power supply and forces it into the tank circuit. C_4 is the blocking capacitor which keeps the DC plate voltage out of the tank circuit but allows the RF to get through.

The grid capacitor C_1 and resistor R_1 bias the grid. These are in shunt rather than in series with the crystal in order to keep down the amount of voltage across the plates of the crystal power input. Shunt feed is used, through the inductor L_2 to plate of the tube.

RFC_1 is the grid choke which keeps down the current flow in the crystal circuit. In the absence of RFC_1, the RF being generated by the crystal would be shorted by C_1 to ground. An excessively large current would flow in the tank circuit, causing the crystal to vibrate so strongly as to overheat, and possibly crack or shatter.

Review of TPTG and Crystal Oscillators

THE TPTG OSCILLATOR—uses a tuned circuit in both the plate and grid circuits. Maximum power output is obtained when the plate tank circuit is tuned to the same resonant frequency as the grid tank circuit.

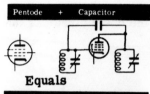

FEEDBACK—can be provided by means of link coupling or a capacitor when a pentode is used. The plate-to-grid capacitance provides feedback when a triode is used.

A CRYSTAL—with its conducting plates is equivalent to a parallel resonant circuit, and can be used in place of the grid tank circuit of the TPTG oscillator.

CRYSTAL OSCILLATOR—is very similar to the TPTG oscillator, but uses a crystal in place of the grid tank circuit. Power output is low, but frequency stability is excellent where only one frequency is required.

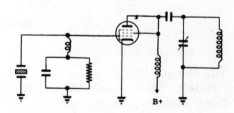

POWER OUTPUT—of the crystal oscillator is maximum when the plate tank is tuned to the natural mechanical frequency of vibration of the crystal. The oscillator is usually operated at less than maximum power output to achieve stability of operation.

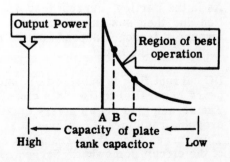

Introduction to the Electron-Coupled Oscillator

The Colpitts and Hartley oscillators are good all-round oscillators, but they do not quite meet the needs of good frequency stability. The crystal oscillator has good frequency stability, but it is limited to relatively low power output and to a single frequency of operation plus its harmonics. What is still needed is an oscillator having good frequency stability in addition to high power output and a wide operating range. One which meets all three conditions is the electron-coupled oscillator. As a result, it is very widely used, at moderate frequencies, in transmitters.

Below is the basic circuit of the electron-coupled oscillator, or ECO.

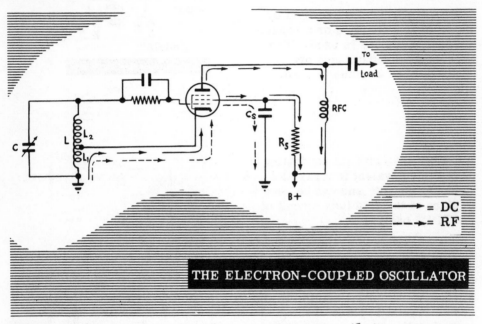

THE ELECTRON-COUPLED OSCILLATOR

You can see that this is a modified Hartley oscillator. The modification consists in the replacement of the triode by a tetrode, which has an additional element, the screen grid.

As in the Hartley, current feedback across L_2 starts the cycle of oscillation and then sustains it in the LC tank. As in the Hartley, too, the amount of feedback depends on the ratio of L_1 to L_2. Thus the method of feedback is the same.

DC current flow is substantially unchanged except that a screen circuit appears in parallel to the plate circuit as shown by the arrows in the diagram. The screen grid draws a very small portion of the total current since a dropping resistor, R_8, places it at a much lower potential than the plate. This screen current represents a small power loss, reducing the efficiency of the circuit somewhat. Screen current may be about three ma. as compared to approximately sixty ma. in the plate circuit.

The ECO Circuit

In the electron-coupled oscillator, the cathode, control grid and screen grid form a series-fed Hartley oscillator with LC as its oscillatory circuit. The screen grid serves as the plate of the oscillator. The screen draws only a small portion of the electron stream through the tube—only enough to support oscillation. This RF current is coupled back to the oscillator tank through C_s, the screen grid RF bypassing capacitor.

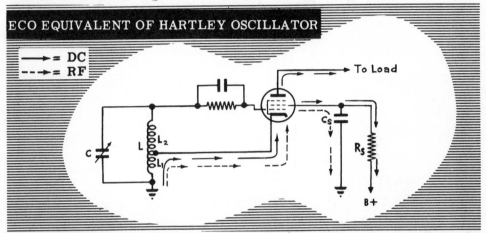

ECO EQUIVALENT OF HARTLEY OSCILLATOR

From the diagram it can be seen that both DC and RF paths are identical with DC and RF paths in the Hartley oscillator.

There are two consequences to these changes in feedback:

1. It means that the plate has been isolated from the LC circuit connected to the tube. The screen, being effectively grounded for RF potentials by capacitor C_s, shields the plate from the portions of the tube connected to the LC circuit. The plate is only an output electrode to the load.

    It also means that many electrons will pass through the positive screen because they are attracted to the more positive plate. The electron current going to the plate is increased and decreased by the action of the grid, but the plate has no significant effect upon this electron current. Therefore the plate current will have an AC component due to the oscillator, this AC component being of the same frequency as that of the oscillator. Thus energy is delivered to the load through the electron stream within the tetrode—the coupling medium is the electron stream, hence the name "electron-coupled oscillator."

2. For the oscillator, it means that this section has been shielded from what occurs in the output or load circuit. Therefore, changes of load impedance will not affect the oscillator. Also, so long as the ratio of plate and screen voltages remains the same—which is assured by taking both from the same source through a voltage divider—voltage on the plate cannot affect the oscillator.

The ECO Circuit (continued)

From the diagrams, it can be seen that in the Hartley oscillator—and in the other oscillators, except the crystal oscillator using a tetrode—the LC tank determines the frequency of oscillation and supplies power to the load. Hence, any change of load was reflected into the LC circuit and produced a frequency shift. In the ECO, the LC tank determines the frequency but the plate delivers power to the load. So load changes are not reflected back into the LC tank.

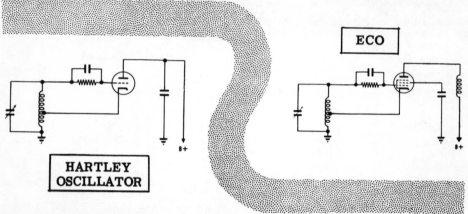

The oscillator section of the electron-coupled oscillator may be a Colpitts circuit instead of a Hartley circuit with equally satisfactory results. The "electron-coupling" effect refers to how energy is delivered from oscillator to plate circuit, not to how the oscillations are generated.

The only difference between the Colpitts ECO and the Hartley ECO lies in the feedback circuit to sustain oscillation. Capacitance, instead of inductance, is tapped.

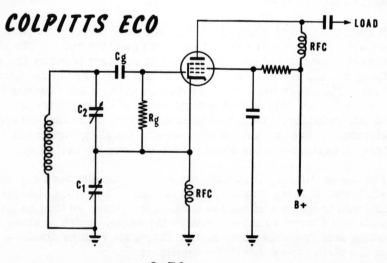

Analysis of the ECO

Shown below is a Colpitts type ECO. Its operation is almost identical with that of the Hartley ECO which was explained previously.

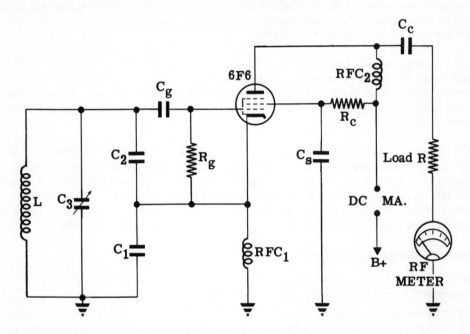

A pentode connected as a tetrode is used in place of the triode of the Colpitts oscillator. The cathode, control grid and screen, along with the tank circuit, act as a conventional Colpitts oscillator. The screen RF by-pass capacitor, C_s, shields this triode from the plate and supplies feedback across C_1, the AC screen grid load.

The tank circuit is C_1-C_2-C_3-L. C_3 has been placed in parallel with C_1-C_2 so that the tank can be tuned without changing the ratio of C_1 to C_2.

RFC_1 is necessary for oscillations to be sustained. It prevents an RF short circuit from C_s back to cathode, in which case feedback would never reach the tank circuit.

Most of the electrons leaving the cathode reach the plate which is at a higher potential than the screen grid. The AC component of plate current is coupled to the load by capacitor C_c, while RFC_2 blocks this same AC (RF) current from the B+ supply. Thus the plate of the tube acts as an output electrode, its function being to deliver power to the load. Electron coupling within the tube delivers power to the plate circuit. This does not alter the way in which feedback is coupled back to sustain oscillations.

The Colpitts type ECO is relatively immune to changes of load and plate voltage.

3-77

Variations in Oscillators—Series and Shunt Feed

In previous topics you examined the Armstrong, Hartley, electron-coupled, Colpitts, tuned-plate tuned-grid, and crystal oscillators. Each one of the circuits you have already studied can be set up in a number of ways. Then there are probably a dozen other types of oscillators, each of which may be connected in a number of ways.

The reason for all these oscillator circuits is that various circuits have different advantages as well as disadvantages. Certain oscillators are more stable than others. Some are less affected by loading. Others are just simpler, and thus easier, to include in the equipment for which they are designed.

One possible variation in an oscillator circuit is the choice between series feed and shunt feed. Series feed is a hookup in which the plate current flows through the tank coil. In shunt feed, the plate current flows through an RF choke, and only RF current flows through the tank. Here is how the Hartley oscillator is connected for series feed and shunt feed. Nearly every other oscillator circuit may be varied in a similar manner.

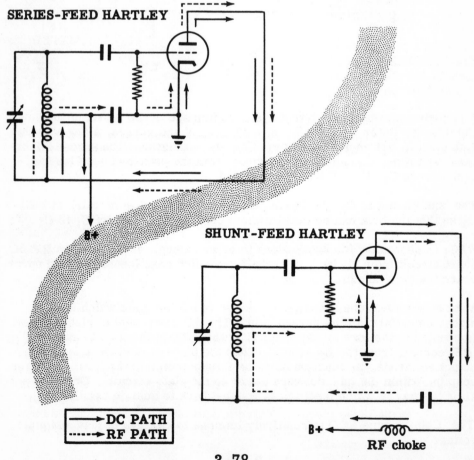

SERIES-FEED HARTLEY

B+

SHUNT-FEED HARTLEY

DC PATH
RF PATH

B+

RF choke

Variations in Oscillators—RF Ground Potential

Any point in an oscillator or RF amplifier circuit which has a high impedance to ground with respect to RF is said to be "above RF ground potential."
Any point which presents a low impedance to ground for RF current is
said to be "at RF ground potential."

Below, you see a circuit of a Hartley oscillator. You will notice that the
cathode does not go directly to ground. There is a coil between the cathode and ground. This coil presents some impedance to RF. Therefore,
the cathode is not at ground potential with respect to RF. It is above RF
ground potential.

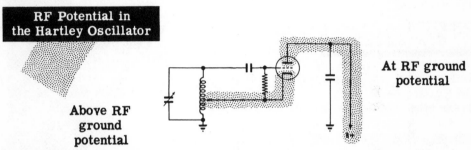

**RF Potential in
the Hartley Oscillator**

At RF ground
potential

Above RF
ground
potential

There is a capacitor between the plate of the Hartley oscillator and ground.
This capacitor offers a very low impedance path for RF. Since it goes to
ground, the plate is considered at RF ground potential, even though it is
at a high DC potential.

A circuit diagram of the Armstrong oscillator is shown below. The cathode is at RF ground potential. It has a low impedance connection to
ground—a wire. The plate is above RF ground potential because it is
connected to B+ through a coil and B+ is always at RF ground potential.

Above RF
ground
potential

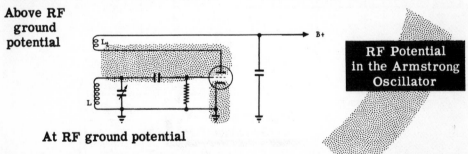

B+

**RF Potential
in the Armstrong
Oscillator**

At RF ground potential

The grid of the Armstrong oscillator is above ground potential even though
there is a capacitor between grid and ground. This is because the capacitor is connected across a coil. The combination of capacitor and coil
form a parallel-resonant circuit which has a high impedance to RF at its
resonant frequency. The Armstrong circuit oscillates at the resonant
frequency of the tuned circuit. Therefore, as long as the circuit is oscillating, there is a high impedance from grid to ground so that the grid is
above RF ground potential.

Variations in Oscillators—Different Grounding Points

You have already seen that the Hartley oscillator may be connected for series or shunt feed. You probably noticed that the cathode goes directly to ground in both circuits. Any oscillator using a triode must have at least two of its three electrodes (cathode, grid and plate) above RF ground potential. The third electrode may be at RF ground potential. This produces three more variations in an oscillator circuit. These variations are illustrated below in the Colpitts circuit. The three hookups shown use shunt feed. Most other oscillators can be connected with the cathode, grid, or plate at RF ground potential.

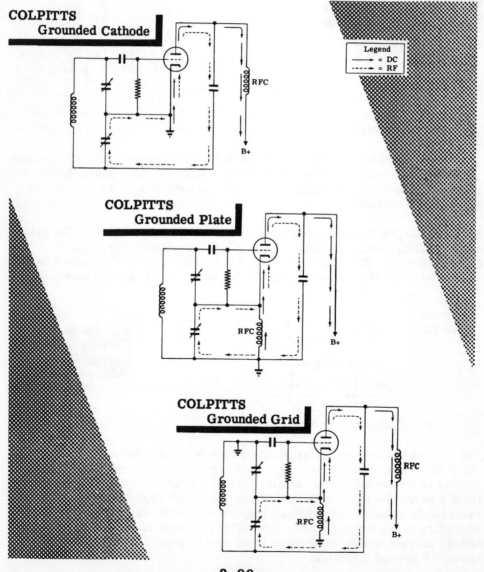

COLPITTS
Grounded Cathode

Legend
= DC
= RF

RFC

B+

COLPITTS
Grounded Plate

RFC

B+

COLPITTS
Grounded Grid

RFC

RFC

B+

Variations in Oscillators—Other Circuits

The oscillator circuits shown below are included so that you can become accustomed to analyzing many different forms of oscillators. They are all variations on the six basic oscillators which you studied in previous topics, except for the klystron oscillator, the principle of which is explained in the text.

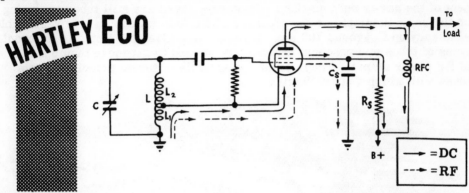

The most important thing to remember about oscillators, no matter what kind, is that they all must have certain features:

1. Something which couples the output to the input.
2. Something which corrects the phase of the voltage fed back.

Here are some other oscillator circuits. See if you can locate the source of feedback. Then trace the DC and RF paths.

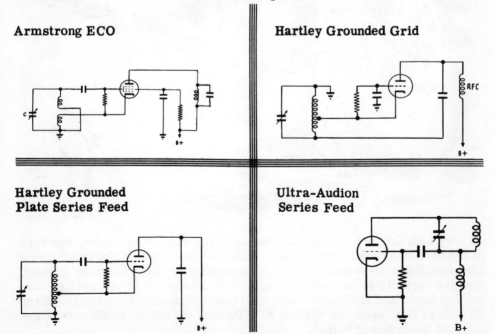

Armstrong ECO

Hartley Grounded Grid

Hartley Grounded
Plate Series Feed

Ultra-Audion
Series Feed

High Frequency Oscillators

You have studied the basic oscillators used at low radio frequencies. These operate at high efficiency up to about 20 mc. Beyond 20 mc their efficiency drops unless specially designed high frequency tubes are used. Also the Q of the tuned circuits drops at high frequencies. This loss of efficiency becomes greater, until at 100 mc most tubes will lose fifty per cent of the power put into them. However, there are still tubes operating on the same principle as the ordinary 6C5 triode which can give reasonable efficiency up to around 700 mc. Beyond that—give up! Entirely different types of tubes and resonant circuits are needed to get more than 5 watts of RF power output. They operate on entirely different principles from those with which you are familiar.

At very high frequencies the inductance of the connecting wires, and even of the tube leads, becomes greater than the inductance in the tuned circuit. Likewise, the grid-to-plate and grid-to-cathode capacity becomes greater than the capacity in the tuned circuit. The solution is to use shorter connecting leads and miniature tubes with low interelectrode capacity. Even then, these tiny tubes are useless at 1000 mc. Besides, small tubes cannot give much power output.

3-82

Tuned Lines

At frequencies between 100 and 500 mc, it is still possible to get reasonable power from an oscillator using triodes with special tuned circuits. Instead of having coils with turns and capacitors with parallel plates, tuned lines, which are the equivalent of a coil and capacitor at low frequencies, are used.

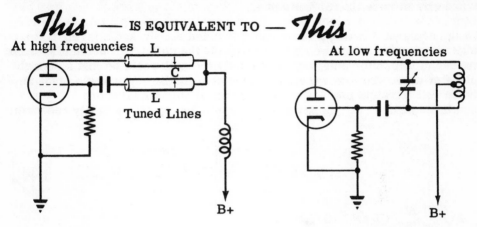

This — IS EQUIVALENT TO — *This*

The characteristics of these tuned lines are calculated in the same way as characteristics of transmission lines, which you will find out about in "Transmitters." Inductance and capacitance of ordinary coils and capacitors is said to be "lumped." Inductance and capacitance of tuned lines is said to be "distributed." Here are some other high frequency oscillator circuits using distributed reactance (capacity and inductance).

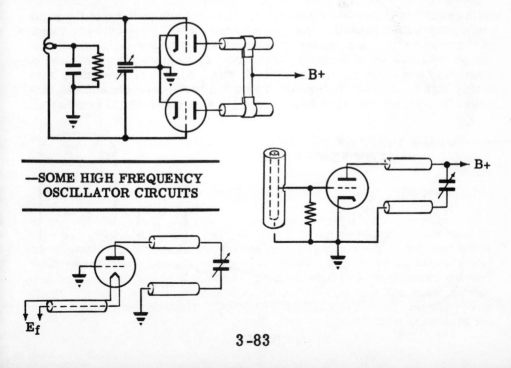

—SOME HIGH FREQUENCY
OSCILLATOR CIRCUITS

Cavity Resonators at Ultra-high Frequencies

You have learned that the connecting leads between the tube and the tuned circuit have more reactance than the tuned circuit itself at high frequencies. One solution to this difficulty would be to eliminate the connecting leads by putting the tuned circuit inside the tube. What shape would the tuned circuit have then? Let's see.

Imagine yourself taking a low frequency tuned circuit and altering it for high frequencies. You would take turns off the coil. You would also make the tuning capacitor smaller. Eventually, the coil would be just a straight piece of wire. To lower the inductance still further, you would place another coil (straight piece of wire) in parallel with the first one. If you continued adding coils in parallel you would end up with a cavity resonator.

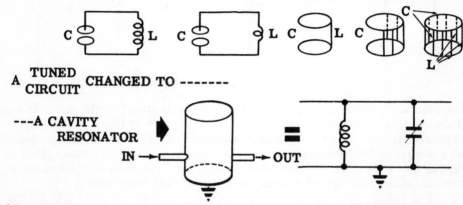

A TUNED CIRCUIT CHANGED TO -------

---A CAVITY RESONATOR

IN → → OUT

This cavity resonator is cylindrical in shape. If you performed the same conversion with a capacitor that has squares plates, you would get a square cavity resonator. As a matter of fact almost any hollow metal structure can perform the job of a cavity resonator. Certain shapes are chosen because they are more convenient to work with. All cavity resonators have a very high Q, often 20 times higher than the best conventional tuned circuits. Remember that they do the same job as a conventional tuned circuit.

OTHER TYPES OF
   CAVITY RESONATORS

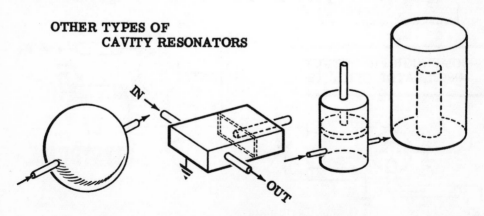

The Klystron Tube

The klystron is a vacuum tube operating on an entirely different principle from conventional tubes. It can be made to amplify or oscillate. Its function as an oscillator is important at this point. Electrons leave the hot cathode and are accelerated by a positive grid. They fly toward a buncher, which is a pair of grids at the same positive potential as the accelerator. They reach the nearer of the two buncher grids first and deliver a kick to the tuned circuit, which starts it oscillating. By the time the first group of electrons reaches the second buncher grid, its potential has changed because of the oscillations in the tuned circuit. When the second buncher grid swings in a negative direction, fewer electrons get through. When it swings in a positive direction, more electrons get through. Although the electrons approach the buncher uniformly spaced, they leave the buncher in clusters. This is similar to the increase and decrease of plate current in a conventional oscillator.

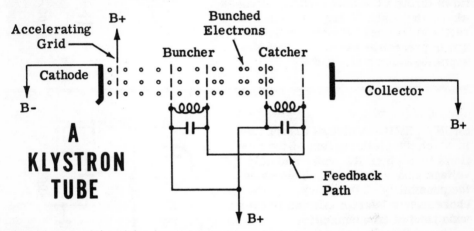

Then these bunched electrons reach the catcher grids and start the second tuned circuit oscillating. Since they keep arriving in bunches, they keep the second tuned circuit oscillating. The oscillations in the first tuned circuit will stop unless voltage is fed back from the catcher grids to keep it going. Of course the tuned circuits in the klystron are not coils and capacitors. They are cavity resonators.

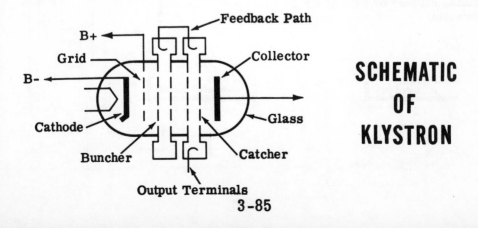

Review of High Frequency Oscillators

The description of the klystron tube was not included to make you into a klystron expert. There are other types of klystron tubes, and different circuits, too complex to be discussed at this point. The purpose of this description was to acquaint you with what sort of techniques are used at frequencies above the limit of conventional triodes. The klystron can operate efficiently above 10,000 mc. If you study radar you will learn about another ultra-high frequency oscillator, the magnetron. This tube can deliver millions of watts of RF power at 3000 mc and higher.

SERIES FEED—A circuit arrangement in which the plate current of the tube flows through the tank circuit. In cases where the plate of the tube goes directly to the tank, the entire B+ voltage is present at the tank. This presents the danger of shocks.

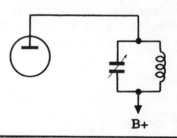

SHUNT FEED—A circuit arrangement in which the plate current of the tube flows through an RF choke and only RF voltage gets to the tank. This avoids the possibility of DC shock, but the RF choke cannot operate efficiently over a wide band of frequencies.

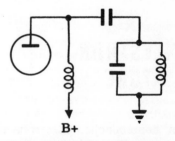

GROUNDING POINTS—Most oscillator circuits can be made to work with the plate, cathode or grid at RF ground potential.

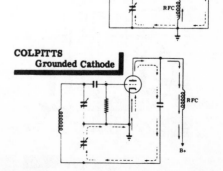

COLPITTS
Grounded Plate

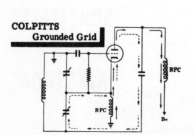

COLPITTS
Grounded Grid

COLPITTS
Grounded Cathode

Review of High Frequency Oscillators (continued)

ECO—The ECO is not a special type of oscillator. It is a circuit in which a screen-grid tube is used instead of a triode. The screen grid is the oscillator anode. It is at RF ground potential and therefore isolates the oscillator from the output circuit. Changes in loading have less effect on the frequency of oscillation.

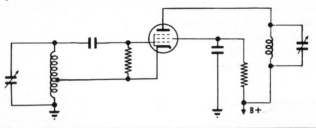

LUMPED REACTANCE—All standard coils and capacitors are lumped reactances.

DISTRIBUTED REACTANCE—Obtaining capacity or inductance from straight wires. Generally, parallel wires are used. At high frequencies, it becomes necessary to use distributed reactances because they have a higher Q than ordinary coils and capacitors.

CAVITY RESONATOR—A hollow metal structure which exhibits the same characteristics at high frequencies as a coil and capacitor at low frequencies. It has a much higher Q than an ordinary coil and capacitor.

KLYSTRON—A vacuum tube designed to operate at frequencies above 1000 mc. It has several forms, all of which use a positive grid as an accelerator and other grids to bunch the electrons together in clusters.

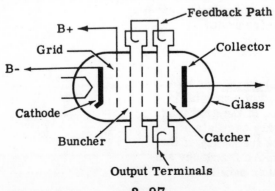

Review of Oscillators

ELECTRONIC OSCILLATOR—A
vacuum tube amplifier with a feedback
circuit either internal or external to
the tube. It generates continuous sine
wave AC of a controllable frequency.
It has a tuned circuit which does the
oscillating and controls the frequency
of the wave generated. The vacuum
tube merely supplies pulses to keep
the tuned circuit oscillating.

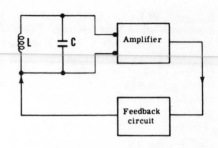

ARMSTRONG OSCILLATOR—uses a
tickler coil to feed back pulses from
the plate circuit to the tank circuit.

HARTLEY OSCILLATOR—uses a
tapped coil instead of a separate tickler
winding to feed back pulses. It has
more frequency stability than the
Armstrong.

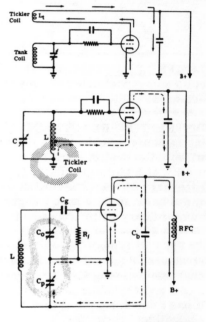

COLPITTS OSCILLATOR—uses a
tapped capacitance network to couple the
pulses to the tank. It has more frequency stability than the Hartley.

TPTG OSCILLATOR—uses the grid-
plate capacitance of a triode to feed
back pulses to a tuned circuit connected to the grid. It oscillates only
when the two tuned circuits are set to
or near the same frequency.

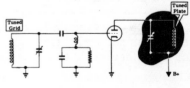

CRYSTAL OSCILLATOR—is like a
TPTG oscillator, but a crystal is
connected in place of the grid tank
circuit. It can only oscillate at, or
very close to, the frequency of the
crystal. It has more frequency stability than any other oscillator.

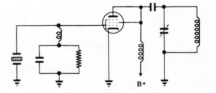

Review of Oscillators (continued)

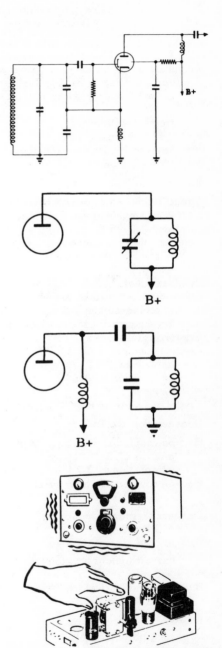

ELECTRON-COUPLING—is a method of connecting other oscillator circuits. In the electron-coupled oscillator, the screen grid is the feedback electrode, leaving the plate independent of the oscillator section. Changes in load and plate voltage have little effect on oscillator frequency. It is more stable than any other oscillator except the crystal.

SERIES FEED—a circuit arrangement in which the plate current of the tube flows through the tank circuit. In cases where the plate of the tube goes directly to the tank, the entire B+ voltage is present at the tank. This presents the danger of shocks.

SHUNT FEED—a circuit arrangement in which the plate current of the tube flows through an RF choke, and only RF voltage gets to the tank. This avoids the possibility of DC shock, but the RF choke cannot operate efficiently over a wide band of frequencies.

FREQUENCY STABILITY—the ability of an oscillator to keep putting out the same frequency when it is subjected to changes in load and plate voltage, heat, humidity, vibration, etc.

INDEX TO VOL. 3

(Note: A cumulative index covering all five volumes
in this series will be found at the end of Volume 5.)